THE INHABITED UNIVERSE

By Kenneth W. Gatland

DEVELOPMENT OF THE GUIDED-MISSILE

By Kenneth W. Gatland and Anthony M. Kunesch

SPACE TRAVEL

One of the most incredible astronomical photographs ever taken, the colliding galaxies in Cygnus. Two immense star-packed galaxies, a "globular" and a "spiral" have met in their huge wanderings, yet so far apart are the individual stars they contain that few, if any, will collide.

Mt. Wilson and Palomar Observatories.

THE INHABITED UNIVERSE

An inquiry staged on the frontiers of knowledge

by

KENNETH W. GATLAND, F.R.A.S.

and

DEREK D. DEMPSTER, M.A. Cantab.

Illustrated with photographs, and drawings by John W. Wood

DAVID McKAY COMPANY, INC.
New York

Made and Printed in Great Britain
by
THE WHITEFRIARS PRESS LTD.
LONDON AND TONBRIDGE

CONTENTS

ILLUSTRATIONS

"It will ever remain incomprehensible that our generation, so great in its achievements of discovery, could be so low spiritually as to give up thinking."

ALBERT SCHWEITZER

Life and Thought

INTRODUCTION

LOOKING BACK in time, we see man as a creature of the forest sharing his environment with other fauna. Then, no one knows quite how or when the spark that was to raise him above the lesser animals and enable him to take charge of his affairs flickered within him. The gradual development of the human brain had begun.

Man's ability to reason, later coupled with the development of language, led to all kinds of pursuits that emphasized his supremacy. The ability to make and use weapons, the making of fire, the development of agriculture which ultimately led to the founding of settled communities—these things gave man leisure, social intercourse, and a degree of cultural progress.

The phenomenal rise of man had been due to the fact that evolution was taking place on an intellectual level and not merely a biological one; the human brain was developing as a result of man's self-willed powers of observation and inquiry.

Through the early civilizations, Egyptian, Sumerian, Minoan, Sinic, Mayan, Andean, Greek and Roman, and many others, he evolved a greater culture.

Then came the Western civilization which blossomed into a swift-flowing pageant of discoveries and inventions. The harnessing of steam paved the way for the Industrial Revolution which in turn stimulated human inventiveness in whose wake sprang the steam locomotive, the internal combustion engine, the jet plane, radio and television, finer medicine and surgery, and speedier transport. Man's conquest of his environment became so pronounced that it seemed he could answer everything—nothing was beyond his powers of achievement. The world was his and he would not rest until all its secrets were known. Now man appeared to stand at the head of knowledge. Even the secret of the atom had been pierced. The world itself trembled at his approach!

But what if knowledge became his master and destroyed

him? Suddenly, there seemed to be so little time; realization dawned that man was at once master and executioner. Had evolution produced an unbalanced creature—an intellectual monster—with all the tendencies for ending its days in an evolutionary blind-alley?

Just as the dinosaurs of a bygone age were destined to become extinct because they could not adapt themselves to a changing environment, so in the age of the hydrogen-bomb man had provided for himself an enviroment in which the end of the human animal could be equally inevitable. It would be ironic indeed if the hydrogen-to-helium reaction, which has maintained the sun's temperature for 5,000 million years, making life possible on this planet, were in the end to be the means which finally destroyed that life.

Life is everywhere around us. We are part of it. Yet, for all our scientific advancement, it is the thing we understand least.

A biologist will tell you that life arose perhaps more than 1,500 million years ago in the warm waters of the cooling earth. It is supposed that simple substances, such as water and carbon dioxide, were combined into more complex compounds—amino acids and proteins—by the action of sunlight. A physicist will qualify these remarks by pointing out that so-called "non-living matter" and "living matter" are indistinguishable in the world of the atom, and that all matter has its basis in energy.

To this, a philosopher might add cynically that life finds its highest biological expression in man, the most quarrelsome creature in the whole pageant of evolution. Yet man alone has the capacity to reflect upon himself and question his destiny.

A theologian's view will be that man is immortal and can never be regarded as the product of blind forces within the universe.

Who are we? Where do we come from? Whither are we bound?

ACKNOWLEDGEMENTS

A BOOK which casts its net so wide and so deep as " The Inhabited Universe " cannot be written without the help of specialists in many fields. In the more than two years it has taken to write and the several years of study before thoughts were committed to paper, the paths of inquiry have led me to a number of subjects whose true nature I had previously been only dimly aware. To all those in diverse fields who, consciously and unconsciously, have aided this study, I should like to record my sincere gratitude.

Particularly am I indebted to Mr. Patrick Moore for his kindness in reading the astronomical chapters and for valuable comments and suggestions. A great deal of Mr. Moore's personal researches on Mars is incorporated in Chapter Three, while Dr. Alan E. Slater's own studies, concerning possible Martian vegetation, have been an equally useful reference.

In the sphere of biology, I should like to thank Mr. Eric Horning, Professor of Experimental Pathology, the Chester Beatty Research Institute, the Royal Cancer Hospital, for a fascinating (and instructive) afternoon spent in the company of his staff engaged in cancer research. It is a sobering thought that some of the most vital discoveries concerning life's beginnings would not have been made but for the necessity for research into the causes of disease. I am also grateful to Mr. R. J. Goldacre of the Chester Beatty Research Institute, who has made a special study of the origins of life, for the loan of data and manuscripts. In addition, the staff of the Natural History Museum, South Kensington, have been most helpful; in particular a lady specialist in protozoa, who perforce must be nameless in deference to Civil Service protocol.

To the following, I should like to express my thanks for illustrations : *Dr. John Postgate*, for the micrograph of sulphate-reducing bacteria, reproduced by permission of the Director, Chemical Research Laboratory, Teddington. *Professor R. C.*

Williams, of the Virus Laboratory, University of California, for the micrographs of human poliomyelitis virus, tobacco mosaic virus, and bacterium of E. colic. *Mr. R. A. Fox* (and Professor Michael Swann), of the Department of Zoology, University of Edinburgh, for the micrograph of a cell in division; (also, the editor of *The Times Science Review*, in whose paper the illustration originally appeared). *Professor Erwin Müller*, Department of Physics, Pennsylvania State University, for three photographs depicting his own experiments in which, for the first time, individual atoms were photographed. *The Director and Secretary*, the Science Museum, South Kensington, for the diagram showing the penetrative effect of cosmic rays. *Mt. Wilson and Palomar Observatories*, for various astronomical photographs obtained with the 200-inch telescope (also, Mr. Bruce Lansbury who expedited their dispatch from America). *Miss Joan Turner*, United States Information Service, for the photographs of the Bevatron and Alternating Gradient Synchrotron. *My wife, Doreen*, for the model of a sodium atom and Mr. J. W. Seller for taking the photograph.

It is a great pleasure to acknowledge, once again, my good friend John W. Wood, for his unfailing care in the preparation of the drawings which, from the outset, were considered as an integral part of the book.

My especial thanks are due to Derek D. Dempster, who joined me in writing the last third of the manuscript when other pressing commitments prevented me from completing the work on time; also, for his introduction to the person, and work, of Dr. Rolf Alexander. Our joint gratitude is due to Mrs. Ann Mason for her extreme care in typing—and re-typing—the manuscript, without whose aid, who knows, we might still be lost in a paper jungle.

Kenneth W. Gatland,
Whitton, Middlesex,
May, 1957.

CHAPTER ONE *Worlds in Creation*

> *" And the earth was without form, and void; and darkness was upon the face of the deep . . ."*
>
> GENESIS.

STARS ARE not distributed uniformly throughout the universe. They occur in groups, great star islands each plainly isolated from its neighbours by an immensity of space; these are the galaxies. Our own sun with its nine planets are but tiny fragments of a galaxy which contains millions of suns similar to our own.

Hydrogen, which pervades all space, is believed to be the raw material from which all things are created and it is from this diffused gas that the giant galaxies have condensed, rather as steam will condense into droplets of water on a cold glass plate; yet space is far more empty than the best vacuum that can be produced in a laboratory. Although our knowledge of how galaxies are formed is far from complete, they appear to begin life as tenuous irregular clouds which coalesce and gradually become localized centres of turbulent gas. As more and more interstellar gas is absorbed, eddies and instability within the cloud generate forces which ultimately cause the system to rotate and take on a spiral form.

Although proof of other galaxies beyond our own only became available with modern telescopes, many millions of these objects in various stages of evolution are in view and several hundreds have been clearly observed. The nearest is more than 1,500,000 light years distant and stands in relation to our galaxy as one man stands at forty paces from another.

The appearance of these galaxies is very different. Some appear as lines of light with a central " bulge," some are lens shaped and still more are spirals in which streams of suns and uncondensed hydrogen seem to pour out from the centre like a radiant shower. This variation is due partly to the stage of evolution reached by each of these galaxies and partly to the

Fig. 1. Formation of the galaxies. The dots represent hydrogen atoms in space.

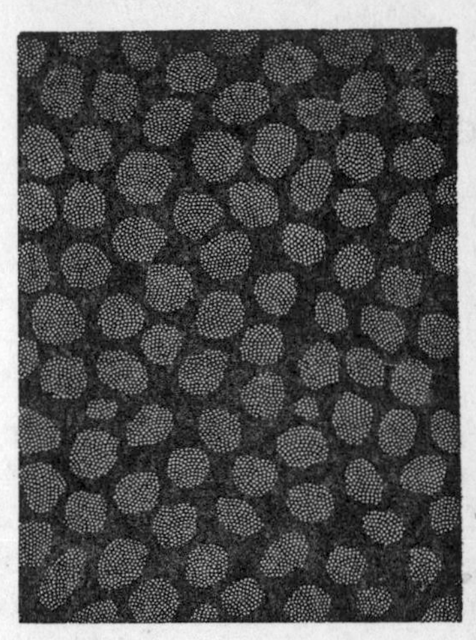

Fig. 2. Here and there tenuous clouds of hydrogen begin to condense out, forming patches of greater density.

angle at which they present themselves to us. A still later phase in evolution is believed to be represented by the globular galaxy (Fig. 5).

If we were to take a look at our own from the outside, it would appear something like the Great Nebula in Andromeda (Fig. 3), a giant wheel of gas and stars turning in space. Each galaxy is separated from its neighbours, but so immense are they that the stars they contain, by their very number, appear to flow and stream, like gas or liquid under the influence of some fantastic centrifugal force: a force that imparts to them the spiral form just as the whirlwind in a sandy locality imparts a spiral motion to the dust it raises. According to calculations our galaxy completes one revolution approximately every 200 million years carrying the solar system at a velocity of approximately 600,000 m.p.h.

The galaxies tend to be irregularly scattered throughout space, our own system, for example, being one of a cluster of about seventeen turning about a radius of about one and a half million light years. Nor are they all the same size; some of the main galaxies (our own included) even have smaller satellites (Fig. 3). On the other hand there are clusters with as many as

Fig. 3. Spiral galaxy in Andromeda. A neighbour to our own galaxy, this immense system is more than 1,500,000 light years distant and probably contains about 100,000 million stars.

Fig. 4. The Whirlpool Galaxy in Canes Venatici.

Mt. Wilson and Palomar Observatories.

(Left). *Space—average density* ·0000000000000-00000000000000001 *gramme of matter per cubic centimetre (according to Hubble), largely hydrogen.*

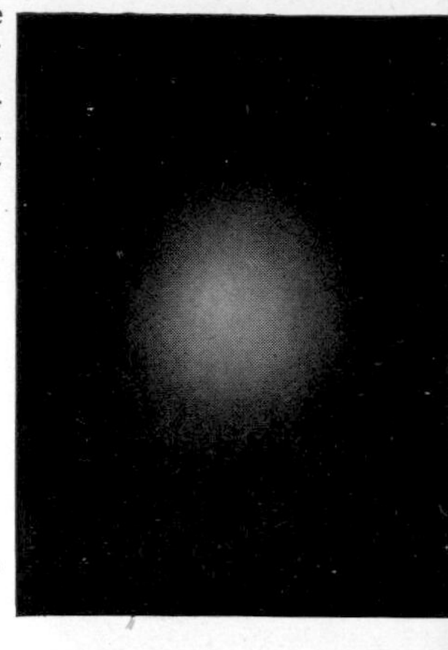

(Right). *An irregular formation of gas.*

(Left). *More and more hydrogen is pulled in from surrounding space, turbulence is set up and the whole structure begins to rotate.*

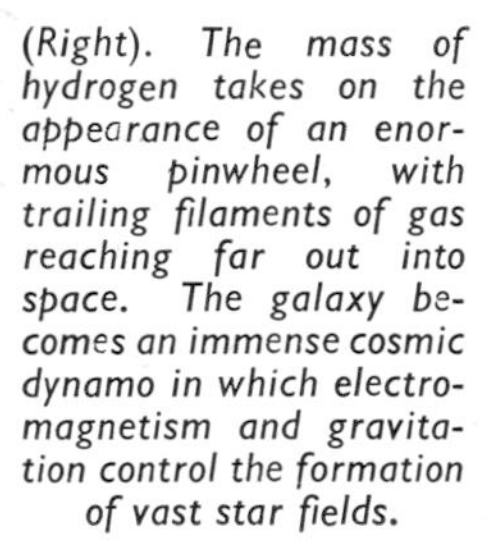

(Right). *The mass of hydrogen takes on the appearance of an enormous pinwheel, with trailing filaments of gas reaching far out into space. The galaxy becomes an immense cosmic dynamo in which electromagnetism and gravitation control the formation of vast star fields.*

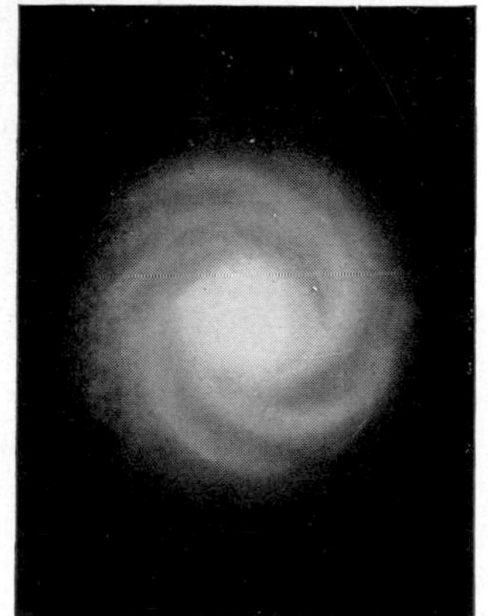

(Left and Right). *A later stage of evolution, it is believed, is represented by the "elliptical" and "globular" galaxies which, seemingly, have contracted under the pressure of their own gravitation.*

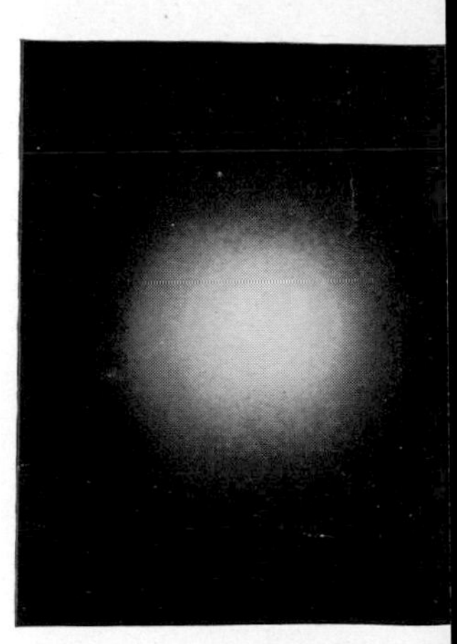

Fig. 5. Evolution of a galaxy.

500 galaxies. In all, about 6,000 million galaxies lie within range of the 200-inch telescope, and remembering that our own galaxy contains, according to recent estimates, about 30,000 million stars, we can only stand in awe at this incredible assembly.

Yet at one time all these galaxies must have contained nothing but whirling gas, and only after clouds had condensed as a result of eddies and gravitational instability—and when many further condensations had taken place within each cloud—would the stars eventually have been born.

Stars are simply dense condensations of gas. To form, the gaseous clouds succumb to the effects of gravitation and shrink with a consequent increase in temperature within them. When this reaches a certain limit the conversion of hydrogen into helium, which follows as a result of nuclear transmutations, triggers off the generation of energy. Eventually the stage is reached where sufficient energy is produced to balance the radiation escaping from the surface whereupon contraction ceases and a new star is born.

So remote are the island galaxies (and even the individual stars of our home galaxy) that everyday terms of measurement such as miles or kilometres are quite useless. In their place the astronomer has adopted a unit of measurement called the "light-year," this being the distance that light, which travels at about 186,000 miles per second, covers in one year—in round figures about 6,000,000 million miles. Therefore, when we say that the nearest star to our solar system, Proxima Centauri, is $4\frac{1}{3}$ light years distant, it means that what we actually observe is not the star but an image which began its journey across the void $4\frac{1}{3}$ years before. And that is the nearest star!

The vastness of our galaxy can best be appreciated if we remember that apart from containing around 30,000 million stars, it is about 100,000 light years in diameter and 10,000 light years thick—and that it is merely our local system! The gulf that separates us from the neighbouring star island in Andromeda exceeds 1,500,000 light years while the most remote galaxies yet photographed (by the 200-inch telescope) are no less than 2,000 million light years away—distances that are utterly beyond our powers of comprehension, beside which our own solar system shrinks to the scale of an atom, the sun its nucleus and the planets circling electrons.

We know that the sun is an ordinary star among several hundred thousand million stars in an island galaxy. Whether or not most of them have planets circling them it is impossible to say because of the incredible distances which separate the individual stars. In fact, so great are these distances that it is quite beyond the powers of our telescopes to resolve such minor objects as planets against the brilliance of the stars themselves.

The sequence of the planets of our solar system is one of the first lessons in astronomy and runs: Mercury, Venus, Earth, Mars, Jupiter, Saturn, Uranus, Neptune and Pluto. These worlds are all alike in a few respects—moving in elliptical orbits, in the same direction round the sun, and all shining by reflected light. However, they differ considerably in detail; and although we think of them casually as being " just a space ship's hop from us " they are actually unbelievably far in plain statute miles.

If we were to take a sphere fifty feet in diameter to represent the sun, Mercury would be a ball two and a half inches in diameter " in orbit " 2,000 yards away. Venus, about three quarters of a mile from our model sun would have a diameter of five and a half inches while Earth, a ball just a fraction larger than Venus, would be found circling a mile off accompanied by a large ball-bearing one and a half inches in diameter orbiting respectfully at a distance of thirteen feet—our moon.

At one and a half miles from the sun would lie Mars, three inches in diameter; at five and a quarter miles the five-foot Jupiter with its moons rotating within twenty feet of it. At nine and a half miles, Saturn, measuring four feet two inches would be surrounded to a distance of thirty feet by its ball-bearing sized moons. Nineteen miles out would spin the twenty-two-inch Uranus, while at thirty miles Neptune, not quite an inch smaller than Uranus, would make its circuit. At forty-one miles would be Pluto; and it would measure about three inches.[1] One cannot help boggling at the thought that the nearest sun at that

[1] Kuiper, working with the 200-inch telescopes, estimates that Pluto's diameter may be only 3,600 miles, smaller in fact than Mars.

scale would be 270,000 miles away, *or further than our moon actually is*!

If the solar system was brought into being accidentally and planets are nothing more than freaks, then life too must be something of a freak. To believe that life emerged from disorder in an otherwise orderly universe is untenable if we are to regard man as an important factor of its design. We may, of course, be entirely wrong in according him so much importance, but we have little choice if human ideals are to be maintained.

If, then, we accept the view that man represents a progressive evolution in the expanding universe, we cannot do otherwise than accept the idea that our solar system was formed in harmony with the universe itself.

Unfortunately, we are far from knowing precisely how the solar system was created and among all the theories which seek to account for it there is none which does not experience some difficulty.

To prove our theory, we must seek evidence of uniformity. There is, in fact, a good deal of such evidence within the solar system. All the planets move round the sun in the same direction and their orbits lie roughly in the same plane. The sun and the planets are rotating and with the single exception of Uranus, which virtually rolls along in its orbit,[1] each has the same direction of spin. Moreover, the direction of spin is in the same sense as the direction of the planets' motion round the sun. Also, the satellites, with few exceptions, orbit their parent planets in the same direction. This cannot be the result of chance and, in fact, is exactly what one would expect if the various bodies were condensed from successively diminishing discs of gas.

The satellites are among the chief offenders to a general acceptance of this theory. Jupiter, for example, has twelve known satellites. The four outermost bodies have retrograde

[1] To be strictly accurate, it would be correct to say that the *type* of rotation is the same as with the other planets, but the angle to the perpendicular is 98 degrees. Actually, this does mean a " reversed rotation " but were the tilt only 9 degrees less, we would say the direction of spin was normal.

motion—they revolve round the planet in the opposite direction to the other eight. Similarly, the outermost satellite of Saturn and the first satellite of Neptune both have retrograde motions.

A possible solution is that these particular bodies were not evolved with their parent planets, but are, in fact, captured bodies. In this event, the satellites' motion would just as likely be retrograde as otherwise. In fact, from the manner in which light is reflected from the Martian satellites, Phobos and Deimos, it is strongly suspected that they are actually large irregular rocky debris from the asteroid belt which, at some time past, were captured by Mars.

Pluto—the sun's outermost planet—also appears to be an offender: it pursues an orbit which is considerably out of plane with the other planets. Dr. Gerard P. Kuiper, of Yerkes Observatory at the University of Chicago, suggests that it is not really a planet at all but that it began life as a satellite of Neptune and "escaped" when the planet contracted and lost some of its mass.

As we shall see, it is now all but certain that *life* has evolved outside our tiny global island. However, to assume that simple life forms have developed throughout the universe without acknowledging the equal likelihood of more advanced forms, of the character of man and superior intelligences seems incongruous. If present indications are correct, planetary formation is not the rare and isolated occurrence that was once supposed; the seed from which life germinates appears to be inherent wherever we see stars and star systems. Does the universe, then, assume the character of an immense spawning ground wherein life is free to evolve in its own particular way, according to the environment? At the moment we can do no more than make our own tentative guesses.

But modern astronomical research is beginning to strengthen our convictions. In 1942, K. A. Strand, at Swarthmore College, Pennsylvania, discovered peculiarities in the orbit of the double-star 61 Cygni which indicated the presence of a third body. Strand calculated the mass of this body "C," and estimated its mass at fifteen or sixteen times that of Jupiter. This is much too low for a star, and so 61 Cygni C is presumably a planet.

Celebrated as being the first star to have its distance accurately calculated (by Bessel in 1838), 61 Cygni itself lies ten and nine-tenths light-years—64,000,000 million miles—away from the earth.

It has also been said that the binary system of Ophiuchi, almost seventeen light-years distant, includes a " planet " with a mass of some twelve times that of Jupiter. There is no reason to suppose that such bodies are uncommon. But with present methods we can expect to detect only very massive planets. A body with the mass of, say, the earth or even Saturn would be quite unable to produce measurable effects upon even a dwarf star such as 61 Cygni B.

How planets are formed is still the subject of controversy. In 1749 the French naturalist Buffon suggested that they had condensed from great splatters of solar gas thrown up into space as a result of a comet crashing into the sun. A later theory transformed the comet into a star and the collision into a near miss; near enough, however, for the trespassing star's gravitational attraction to draw a *filament* of hot gas from the sun which, once in space, cooled down to become planets, half of them attached to the invader and the remainder to their mother sun.

Sir James Jeans supported this theory and although it was popular in the 1930's it is now generally discounted. Hoyle points out that although the sun and the planets contain the same basic chemical elements, they do not have them in the same proportions. The most serious difference is found in the case of hydrogen which is estimated to be a thousand times more abundant in the sun than in the planets. If the Jeans supposition were true, the planets would be chemically quite unlike those we find in our system.

Against this *filament theory* stands the no less vulnerable *nebular theory* suggested by the philosopher Kant in 1755. According to him the sun was once surrounded by a rotating nebula, or envelope, of gas and dust presumed to be the residue of some powerful solar explosion. Centrifugal force caused the nebula to bulge at the equator and cast forth a series of rings which coalesced into the separate objects of the solar system. Similar trends are found in the theories of Laplace and Wright.

The advance towards a more satisfactory conception has been led by the Cambridge mathematician, Dr. R. A. Lyttleton. His theory assumes that at one time the sun was a member of a double star and that the other component broke up as a result of the action of internal forces and became a supernova. The sun lost its companion, but gained instead a disc of gaseous debris : the building materials that went to form the planets.

This, however, is only one of the many theories bearing on the evolution of the planets. Dr. Kuiper suggested in a theory he formulated in 1951 that the same swirling dust clouds which created the sun also gave birth to the planets. He believes that the revolving gaseous material which ultimately became stars often divided to become the binary or double stars that account for at least half the stellar community, and that others split into triplets or even larger families, although like Polaris, the North Star, which is a multiple star, they appear to the eye as a single point of light.

When it comes to systems like our own, which he conjectures number about 1,000 million in the Milky Way alone, Dr. Kuiper departs from the theory presupposing some rare accident like a stellar explosion or near-miss.

Occasionally, he says, the distribution of matter and the balance of forces were such that, instead of splitting, a cloud formed a single nucleus. One was our sun, a glowing infant star surrounded by a revolving disc of primogenial matter the breadth of the solar system. Thus, the concentration of gas in the centre of the disc became denser and denser until it was hot enough to support nuclear reactions. But the great body did not explode in the sense that an H-bomb explodes. It was constrained and tempered by its own massive gravitation. The sun shone brightly emulating the millions upon millions of other suns around it, drenching the proto-planets and the remains of the gaseous disc with heat and light. As the disc spun and grew flatter, the effect of gravity created whorls of denser matter within it. These whorls collided, intermingled and absorbed ever increasing quantities of material until, perhaps over 100 million years, the internal temperatures rose until the nuclei became incandescent under the sheer pressure of their own mass and condensed out: the larger whorls into the planets and the lesser ones into the wandering comets of the outer rim. The pressure of the sun's radiation, Kuiper believes, literally blew gases away from the nearer planets, Mercury, Venus, Earth and Mars, leaving little but rocky cores, while planets further away, Jupiter, Saturn, Uranus and Neptune retained much of the original gas from which they were formed.

One might picture the solar system at this stage as an enormous whirlpool: the infant sun at its centre with a number of secondary whirlpools in the swirling outer section representing the planets. Each secondary whorl would be rotating about the centre of the whirlpool and at the same time revolving within itself. And inside the whorls would be still smaller ones: the moons. In this analogy, we have an explanation of how the planets and other bodies acquired their orbital motion round the sun as well as their independent axial rotation, and how although the character of man had yet to be discerned in the fiery pre-history of the worlds, the interchange of night and day and the gentle passage of the seasons were already assured!

In their passage round the primitive sun, these newly-formed bodies would sweep up enormous quantities of the encircling cloud, gaining still more mass, gravitation and heat until, at last, the material was forged which, in further millenia, was to become the progenitor of life.

How long it took for the incandescent gases of the proto-earth to become molten will never be known, nor is it likely that the precise character of the solar system at this early stage will ever be perfectly understood. There are, however, certain discernible features. The earth was spinning much faster then than it is today; it was closer to the sun and the orbital motion it inherited from the primordial whorl made its passage round the sun much more rapid. The moon, too, was much closer to the earth; barely 10,000 miles away as against the 250,000 miles it is today.

The earth must have remained incandescent and molten for

a very long time, but the moon, being so much smaller, would have been the first to produce a solid crust. For a long time, then, the earth retained the characteristics of a minor sun, but as it continued to tunnel its way through the residue of the gaseous cloud, its surface radiated heat from the material that continually welled up on the convection currents rising from the interior until, at last, parts of its molten substance began to crystallize. It is quite possible that it was not the surface that hardened first, but a secondary layer—an olivine mantle—that congealed before the crust, sealing gradually, in the core, the primeval heat that remains undiminished to this day; all of which allowed the crust to cohere upon an ocean of molten rock substance.

The cauldrons of the earth boiled and bubbled—and slowly, almost imperturbably, the fiery redness that had characterized the planet for several millenia began to change. As lava-like substance spread and thickened, the earth's surface was convulsed with eruptive violence. Great patches of the crust floated on an inferno of molten lava. Enormous spouts of the molten material spewed up from the depths in fantastic cascades of fire carrying with them sulphurous and metallic vapours, superheated steam and other chemicals until a dark, stormy atmosphere, shrouded the face of the young planet. No other scene in geological time could ever have equalled the turmoil of this incredible period—the uprising of great irregular masses of semi-plastic granite which had been pushed up by the erupting under-layers only to sink again and be superseded by other masses, until the new-formed strata thickened and gradually cooled below red-heat, congealed, drifted and finally settled on a submerged floor of basalt beneath the sea of molten lava. Gradually a crust consisting of igneous rocks such as granite, solidified to form the proto-continents of the earth.

Because of its relatively large size in relation to the parent planet, the moon cannot be regarded as a true satellite. The two bodies are more correctly defined as a double planetary system; they rotate around a common centre which is located approximately 3,000 miles from the earth's centre.

The moon, we were taught in school, originated from the

earth. It is supposed that the earth had a faster axial rotation than it has today and that, while its surface was still plastic, this resulted in the planet taking on an elliptical shape. In his interesting book, " Guide to the Moon," [1] Patrick Moore gives an account of the theory that there were, at this time, two main forces acting upon the earth—the tides raised upon it by the sun, and its own natural period of vibration. When these two forces were " in resonance," the tides increased to such an extent that the whole body became first pear-shaped and then dumb-bell-shaped, with one " bell " (the earth) much larger than the other (the future moon). Eventually the neck of the dumb-bell broke altogether, and a new world was born. According to W. H. Pickering, the great rounded hollow which now forms the bed of the Pacific Ocean is nothing more nor less than the scar left in the earth's crust by the breaking-away of the moon, so that our satellite was born at the spot where our greatest ocean now rolls. However, Moore points out that this theory, fascinating though it may be, is now regarded as most improbable, and that it is rejected by nearly all leading investigators.

Another theory, propounded by Von Weizsäcker, supposes that the earth and moon were formed separately after the sun had passed through an unusually dense cloud of interstellar gas and that this left the sun with a gaseous envelope which eventually condensed into the planets. He suggests that the inner statellites of Jupiter, Saturn, Uranus and Neptune were formed inside the atmosphere of their parents, but that the other moons of the solar system, including our own, were the subjects of separate condensations captured by the planets at a later stage.

Throughout the whole of this turbulent period, meteors kept the earth under continuous bombardment, piercing the atmosphere and disappearing into the molten inferno. Believed to be the debris of the building process which went to make the solar system, these meteors are still seen today as *shooting stars*; particles of stone and iron which are usually burnt up by friction with the atmosphere fifty or sixty miles above our heads.

Some authorities suggest that it was as a result of this meteoric bombardment that the moon received the scars we see today—innumerable craters, some fantastically immense, which pock-

[1] Revised edition: Collins, 1957.

mark the lunar surface. But a good many more have serious doubts about it. It is a question over which astronomers and physicists are at greatest variance. On the whole, astronomers argue that the distribution of the craters is against them being formed by meteors and they stress the fact that the similarity between bomb craters and lunar craters—which has been a strong argument of the " meteor school "—does not really mean a great deal as similar effects can be produced by underground explosions. Crater chains and the discovery, in one instance, of over sixty tiny craters on the summit of a lunar mountain, they suggest, could scarcely be the result of chance hits. Vulcanism, in one form or another, is favoured by them, although both theories leave much to be desired by way of detailed explanations.

However the lunar craters came into being, the moon's smaller mass and weaker gravitation—one-sixth that of the earth's—undoubtedly had a great influence on their formation. Cooling of the crust took place much more rapidly and the great majority of craters and mountain ranges must have formed while the surface was still plastic. Like the earth, the moon would have evolved an atmosphere during this time of upheaval but this could not have remained for long because the weakness of the gravitational field allowed it to filter away steadily into space. The roughness and sharpness of the lunar landscape testify to the absence of winds, rains, and other atmospheric activity, which would otherwise have produced a smoother landscape. In fact, when we look at the moon today, we see it as it must have been in the earliest days of its formation, its surface covered with a layer of ash, almost certainly volcanic ash, and some of meteoric origin.

The face of the earth changed slowly, and as the fires began to subside the dark vaporous clouds that had massed overhead prepared to extinguish them for ever. But before the primordial deluge could reach the convulsing surface, it boiled back into the atmosphere as great forks of lightning cut and thrust among the clouds.

Gradually the surface cooled and congealed still further, and as it did the rains began to reach it. Transformed into steam by the surface heat the water in turn caused the thin crust to crack and spew up vast quantities of molten rock. But slowly—no one can say how long it took—the rains gained mastery and beneath the torrid overcast the basins of the earth were filled.

CHAPTER TWO *The Dawn of Life*

> *"We must, however, acknowledge, as it seems to me, that man, with all his noble qualities . . . still bears in his bodily frame, the indelible stamp of his lowly origin."*
>
> CHARLES ROBERT DARWIN
> "The Descent of Man" (1871)

IT WAS a world of perpetual night lit only by vivid lightning flashes and the fiery redness of an eruption. And all the while, from the thick atmosphere of chemical vapours that cloaked the infant planet, a searing rain of hot acids lashed down upon the barren rocks.

How long it took for the turbulent atmosphere to clear no one can tell. But at last the intensity of the deluge diminished; for a while the clouds parted and great primal oceans blinked in the sunlight of the first day.

Yet turbulence and storm continued to sweep the earth's surface. Powerful winds far exceeding hurricane strength lashed the sea into gigantic waves which swept unceasingly across the continents of rock while earthquakes continually threw up new land from the depths. Hard granite was worn down, and the spoils of rock were deposited in giant fissures which remained after the initial cooling to become the channels that carried the waters back to the restless sea. Century upon century the weathering of the rocks continued, and waters of far greater chemical potency than we know today acting as powerful solvents on the crustal surfaces caused rock sediment and chemicals of all kinds to settle in the shallow ocean beds. So much we know—or believe we know—of the earth's beginning. But here the scene becomes clouded and confused.

In the thick canopy of gases above the earth, it is possible that solar radiation or lightning discharge synthesized various organic chemicals which descended with the rains, so that the ancient seas steadily acquired materials such as acetic acid, methyl alcohol and formaldehyde. In this way, it is believed, the earth gradually obtained the "soup of organic compounds" from which a chain of evolution, more fantastic than any that had preceded it, was to find expression. It may have taken a further billion years—and then, in some way we still do not clearly understand, conditions somewhere became favourable for the development of the first protein molecule. The supreme moment had arrived. Out of the cosmic void had come first a spiral galaxy, then a sun (of no particular merit among millions of other suns), and from a whorl of gas surrounding it had condensed a planet—a gaseous sphere that hardened and became moist. Now, the first living thing, a simple molecule, alive and able to reproduce itself, had been created by the apparently blind forces of chemical reaction.

Whether this momentous event in the world's history occurred in some isolated part of the earth or in many places at more or less the same time, it is impossible to say. A likely place would be the heavily silted estuary of a river or the inter-tidal rocks near the shore where sunlight could play its part in synthesizing the chemical compounds. Professor Bernal (1953)[1] believes that the first living molecule may have been built upon a surface of wet, muddy clay. Organic chemicals, he says, are easily absorbed onto such a surface and could interact and form more complex compounds, until a catalyst is formed which can reproduce itself. When such an organic catalyst, or enzyme, as it is called, acts as a "jig" and produces something which can produce another something, and so on, the result is life. Short-wave ultra-violet radiation[2] from the sun would be needed to provide energy for building up the molecules.

Before going further, it would be as well to discover what we mean when we speak of "life." At first thought, the definition seems obvious. Something living grows; something that is not alive does not. It is a question about which one can feel perfectly certain—until one probes a little deeper.

[1] "Evolution of Life in the Universe," by Prof. J. D. Bernal. *Journal of the British Interplanetary Society*, May 1953, pp. 114-18.

[2] It is of interest to note that these radiations are now cut-off from the earth by an ozone layer fifteen to twenty miles from the surface, formed from oxygen which living vegetation has since put into the atmosphere.

If growth is the property of life, then chemical crystals must be alive; crystals grow and even stop growing when they reach a certain size. It could even be said that a fire grows when it is fed with the right materials. Nor is movement a criterion, for under varying conditions of temperature, metals expand and contract. There are many other examples.

The fact is that no one has yet succeeded in producing a definition that satisfies every aspect of life, probably because we have become accustomed to thinking of non-living and living things as distinct and separate entities, rather than considering them as different parts of a continuous whole. Later we shall see that the virus appears to exhibit certain dual characteristics, but by the time we get to that stage of our investigation, we shall find that it becomes exceedingly difficult to make a clear-cut distinction between things that are living and things that are not. In fact, it is only when we come to the higher end of the scale that life becomes at all easy to define. We find that the cardinal features are growth, feeding, reproduction, respiration and excretion. Alongside these we find an instinct for self-preservation, or preservation of the species, a capacity for development, and a tenuous thread of heredity. What, then, *is* life? And how does it come about?

Whereas the structure of the universe depends upon hydrogen, the structure of life depends upon carbon. Carbon is the essential " building block " upon which all living things have been constructed. Why should this be? Life requires atoms which have the ability to form themselves into exceptionally large molecules. It is found, for example, that when atoms of hydrogen, oxygen and nitrogen combine, they produce molecules comprising only a few atoms. When atoms of carbon are added, a remarkable change occurs; the hydrogen, oxygen, nitrogen, and carbon atoms link up to form large molecules which may contain tens of thousands of atoms.

What gives the carbon atom this special property of adhering to other atoms on so large a scale? It appears to be an ordinary atom distinguished by having six planetary electrons; whereas boron and nitrogen, its neighbours in the atomic table, have five and seven electrons respectively—yet the carbon atom is quite unique. This is due to its peculiar atomic structure. It is known as a quadrivalent atom because it has a power of four in forming combinations of atoms, in comparison with others having more or less. It is this quality that gives the carbon atom its tremendous potentiality of creating more complex structures. In fact, the number of possible compounds, based on this versatile atom, actually runs into millions.

Protein was the vital development. They are the most complex molecules known, yet all of them are composed of just a few elements, chiefly carbon, hydrogen, oxygen, nitrogen and sulphur. They are incredibly versatile, and have the ability to combine these few elements into a vast number of different structures.

How protein was evolved is still the subject of controversy. Dr. A. I. Oparin,[1] the eminent biochemist, has suggested that during the early stages of the earth's cooling, carbides were produced which, in the presence of a steaming atmosphere, gave rise to hydrocarbons. A further reaction of the hydrocarbons with ammonia evolved nitrogen derivatives. Oparin believes that the interaction of these various chemicals in the oceans and in the turbulent atmosphere above the earth led to the development of a vast number of organic substances, and eventually to the complex protein molecule. In constant agitation in the chemically rich seas, he suggests that these molecules (forming together and breaking up constantly) underwent chemical changes which enabled them to attract other chemicals necessary to their growth and reproduction.

In 1953, a remarkable experiment was made at the University of Chicago by a student, Mr. Stanley Miller, who showed that amino acids, which are the basis of protein, can be produced under controlled laboratory conditions. The particular line of investigation had been stimulated by the work of Dr. Harold C. Urey whose book, " The Planets, Their Origin and Development," published in 1952, contained a theory on the composition of the earth's primitive atmosphere. Miller set up an apparatus in which the chief constituents of this atmosphere—water, methane, ammonia and hydrogen—were brought together. The water was heated and its vapour allowed to

[1] See also *Proceedings of the National Academy of Sciences,* Vol. 38, pp. 351-63.

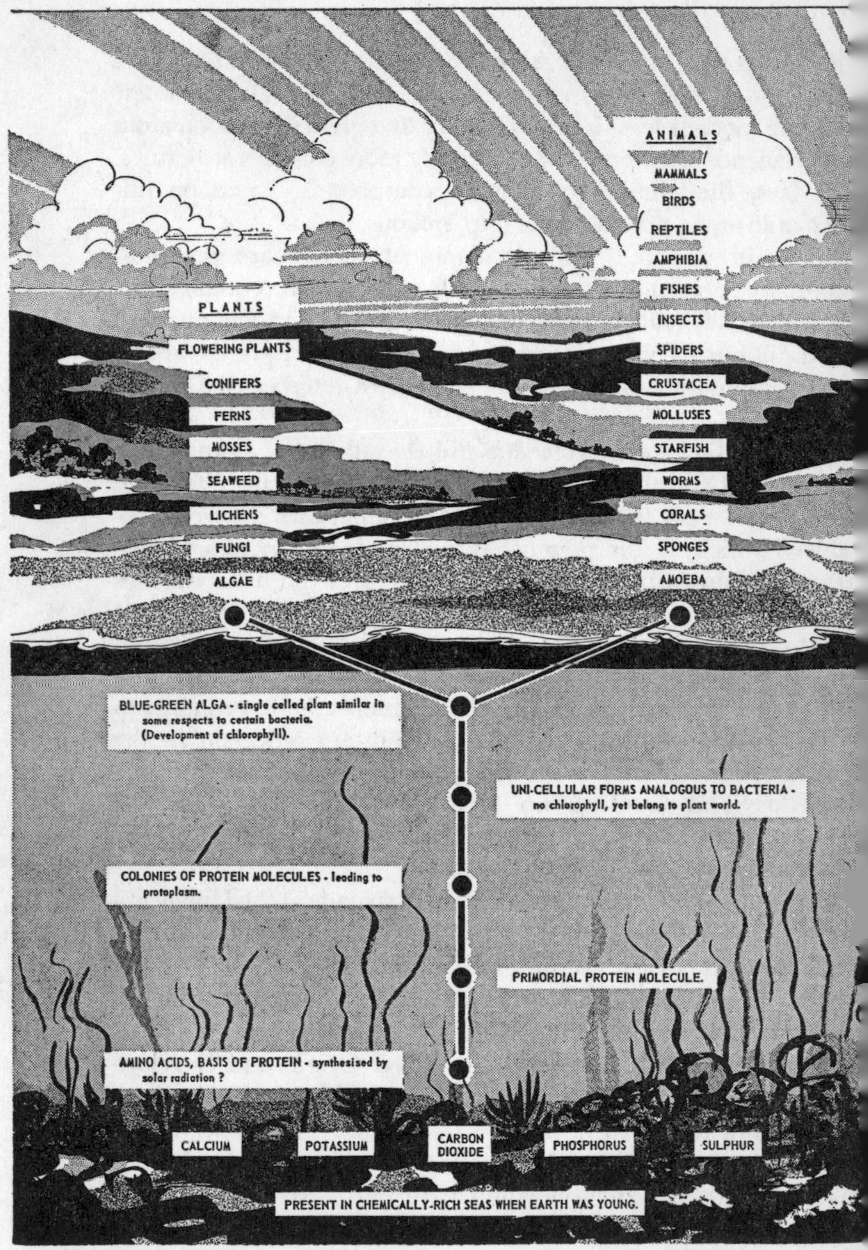

Fig. 6. Diagram showing possible steps in life's evolution from chemical beginnings. one time, it was supposed that uni-cellular organisms, such as amœba, were the m primitive living things ; now, it is recognized that they are specialised offshoots of mo primitive life. Thus, any interpretation of life's beginnings on the basis of what we find the world today must be treated with great reserve.

circulate with the other gases to a point where they were exposed repeatedly to an electric spark. The apparatus was allowed to work continuously for a week; and when the results were analysed, Miller found traces of three amino acids. The experiment seemed a certain proof that the essence from which life evolved was the result of a chemical fusion by some kind of electrical energy, caused by either solar radiation or electric storms.

However, something that may ultimately prove to be of even greater significance, is the result of an experiment by the U.S. Army Quartermaster Research and Development Command, in which amino acids were formed when a solution of ammonium acetate was exposed to atomic radiation.[1]

In the experiment, conducted by Messrs. T. Hasselstrom, M. C. Henry and B. Murr, in 1956, two solutions of ammonium acetate were prepared in water, of 1 per cent. and 2·5 per cent. respectively. Six samples, sealed in polythene bags, were then subjected to varying dosages of beta-rays from a 2-million electron-volt accelerator. When subsequently examined, they were found to contain three amino-acids; glycine, aspartic acid and another not previously identified.

With the greatest dosage of beta-rays, the amount of amino acids present was 1–2 milligrams of each, with more of the unknown acid in the weaker solution. According to the discoverers, the chemical transformation was brought about by the beta-rays decomposing ammonia and water molecules by knocking hydrogen atoms out of them (Fig. 7); the deprived radicals reacted in a variety of ways with the ammonium acetate, forming first glycine and then the more complex amino acids.

There is no reason to believe that substances like ammonium acetate could not have formed when the earth was young, so that although their atomic conversion to amino acids would not be a particularly efficient process under natural conditions, radio-activity in the rocks or perhaps even cosmic radiation, acting over a long period of geological time, might conceivably have worked the " miracle."

In these two results, there is indeed fertile ground for future

[1] *Science*, Vol. 125, p. 350.

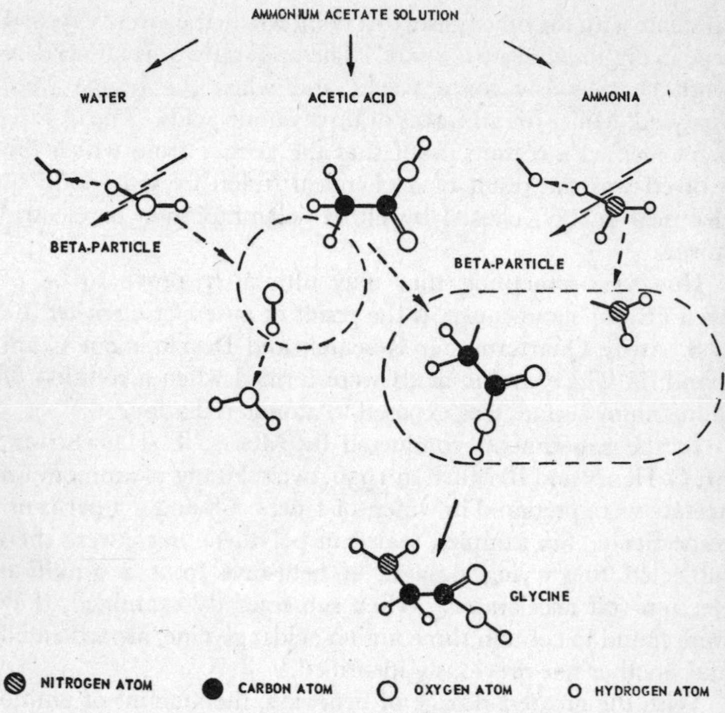

Fig. 7. Diagram illustrating the creation of amino acids by atomic radiation.

research, for once amino acids have been accounted for, the step-by-step approach to the organization and structure of a living cell becomes much easier to explain.

Nevertheless, it would be reasonable to suppose that the cradle of life was the sea. It possessed the nutrient salts in a form which the most delicate organisms could readily assimilate. These salts would have been richest near the shores where primitive rivers emptied into the sea. In these shallow sunlit waters, it is believed, molecules of protein were gradually unified into microscopic bits of protoplasm.[1] No other medium would have been more suitable for the growth and evolution of such fragile and vulnerable forms. The fact that the proportion of salts in

[1] A complex colloidal substance containing largely protein and water.

Fig. 8. Group of four galaxies in Leo, showing different evolutionary stages. Of the galaxies which have been examined with modern telescopes, 80 per cent. are spirals, 17 per cent. are ellipticals and 3 per cent. irregulars. Evolution alone may not account for all the variations that exist; galaxies rotate at different speeds, so that under the influence of centrifugal force, some spirals are less tightly coiled than others.

Mt. Wilson and Palomar Observatories.

Fig. 9. Black sulphurous clouds of steam and other chemical vapours rise from the still molten surface to form the earth's original atmosphere, while continents of rock begin to congeal in layers. Meteors—rocky debris left over from the planets' formation—plummet into the molten interior.

Fig. 10. The second stage in the formation of the earth's crust. While black vaporous clouds mass overhead, the first rains start to fall only to boil back into the atmosphere before they can reach the ground, transformed into steam by the heat of the still plastic surface. But soon, the rains gain mastery—and electric storms rage, perhaps for centuries, filling the basins of the earth to overflowing.

Two of a series of three original paintings by John W. Wood illustrating the formation of the earth.

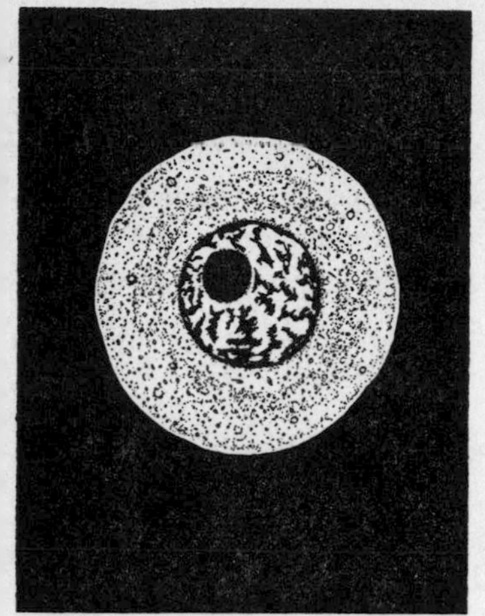

Fig. 11. The primordial cell.

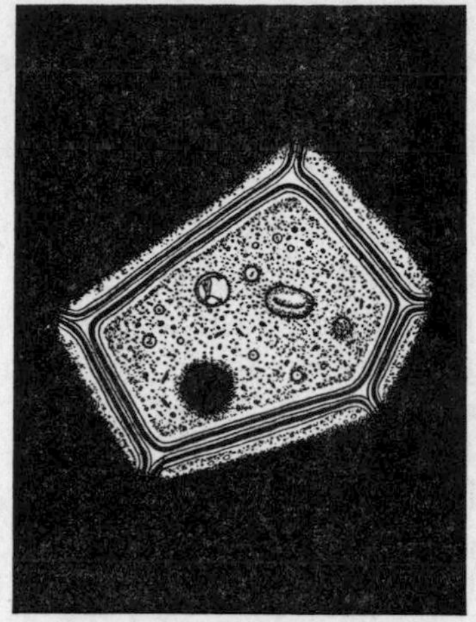

Fig. 12. The living cell—the basis of all life, from the humble amœba to the multi-cellular structure of man.

the blood of animals is approximately the same as it is in sea water lends strong support to this belief.

With infinite slowness, these colonies of protein molecules must have developed into primordial cells of living matter; these were the organisms analogous to bacteria which were able to build up their tissue by living on inorganic substances present in the waters. Exactly what form the proto-life adopted is unknown, though it is certain that the first living organisms were neither plant nor animal.

Is there a link between living and non-living matter? Recent discoveries in micro-biology indicate that crystalline viruses may be near the intermediate stage. In modern life, viruses are responsible for diseases such as influenza, poliomyelitis, common colds, measles—and in plants, tobacco and tomato mosaic. They are able to grow and multiply only within a living cell.

This, of course, is not to suggest that viruses, as they exist today, form the actual " bridge " between the non-living and the living. For one thing, all the known viruses are parasitic within the cells of living things (plants and animals) and are incapable of an independent existence. It is quite impossible to cultivate them in an artificial medium; isolated in a test-tube, they will crystallize, being then incapable of growth or reproduction. However, if subsequently returned to the living cell, they will again take up full metabolic activities.

Had the virus the ability to live freely outside the living cell, its place at the beginning of the evolutionary sequence would no doubt have been assured. But depending as it does on the pre-existence of living things, one must conclude that, at least in its modern form, it is of more recent origin than, let us say, the sulphur bacteria.

All viruses are smaller than the smallest bacteria, and it has been possible to study them in detail only since the advent of the electron microscope. In fact, so minute are these organisms that they cannot be seen at all with any microscope using visible light. The photograph of tobacco mosaic viruses (Fig. 24) was obtained with a magnification of more than 100,000.

If kept in isolation in a test-tube the tobacco mosaic virus will remain dormant for years, having the appearance of a chemical crystal; it will neither grow nor reproduce. But as soon as it is taken out and placed on a tobacco leaf, its character changes and it grows and reproduces exactly like a living organism. Other viruses can be crystallized from solution and after a period of isolation, can be redissolved when they will again multiply and infect living tissue.

Dr. Wendell M. Stanley of the Virus Laboratory, University of California, writes [1]: " It is difficult, if not impossible, to place a sharp dividing line separating living and non-living things when one considers a series of structures of gradually increasing complexity such as hydrogen, water, benzene, egg albumin, insulin, vaccine virus, bacteria. Work on the viruses has provided us with new reasons for considering that life as we know it does not come into existence suddenly but is inherent in all matter."

Striking confirmation of these views came in October, 1955, when Drs. Heinz Fraenkel-Conrat and Robley C. Williams at the Virus Laboratory of the University of California announced

[1] " The Architecture of Viruses," *Physiological Review,* 19, 524, (1939). See also " Some Chemical, Medical and Philosophical Aspects of Viruses," *Science,* 93, 145, (1941).

that they had succeeded in breaking down the tobacco mosaic virus into its constituent chemicals, afterwards reassembling them so that they again became an infectious virus.

How had this been achieved? The tobacco mosaic virus consists of rod-shaped particles, having central cores of nucleic acid with protein molecules strung around them. In the laboratory, virus rods were prepared in solution with dilute alkaline chemicals and maintained at a temperature of almost freezing for between forty-eight and seventy-two hours. After this period, it was found that some of the virus rods had separated into nucleic acid and protein molecules. Those rods which had remained unaffected by this treatment were then removed from the solution by centrifuging. Finally, the protein molecules were precipitated by chemical treatment and, by means of a slightly different technique, the nucleic parts of the virus were successfully isolated.

What the scientists had succeeded in doing was to reduce the component parts of the virus to inert chemicals which, of course, were quite incapable of infecting a tobacco plant. But even more significant was the next stage of their experiment. The two parts of the virus were brought together again in a solution made slightly acid, and left at a temperature just above freezing point for twenty-four hours. At the end of this time, the solution was examined, and the exciting discovery was made that the protein molecules had *rearranged themselves* on the nucleic acid cores. " Inert " chemicals had effectively reformed to produce a living virus.

Moreover, when the virus was introduced into a tobacco leaf, it again became active and, in due course, the characteristic spot of tobacco mosaic virus appeared, signifying growth and reproduction of the reconstituted organism.

Dr. Wendell Stanley, under whose direction the experiment was performed, described the result as " an utterly fantastic discovery on the border-line of life." No less enthusiastic was Dr. Williams, who said he had no doubt that eventually scientists would be able to build the virus in any way they pleased, at least the simple ones, merely by taking the component parts out of laboratory bottles.

Yet the discovery does not end there, for apart from assisting our understanding of the nature of life, it may have great practical importance in man's continual fight against disease. Scientists believe the process may make possible the production of safe and effective vaccines against diseases caused by simple viruses. Dr. Williams has pointed out that only approximately 1 per cent. of the tobacco mosaic viruses reconstructed as a result of the experiment proved fully infectious. This, it is believed, was because not all the protein molecules had rearranged themselves properly on the nucleic cores, so that some of the viruses were no longer perfect and as a result lost much of their power to infect the tobacco plant. If this rebuilding process can be controlled, it is possible that the slightly imperfect viruses produced, while being powerless to start a real infection, could stimulate the defensive forces of the living organism. Furthermore, there seems no reason why the process might not be extended to virus diseases in man, such as polio and influenza.

This is just one of the exciting possibilities which scientists are opening up in the field of bio-chemistry. Already, Dr. Wendell Stanley has suggested that in a similar way as the virus has been reconstructed it may be possible to reproduce chromosomes; by this means, he believes we may learn the secret of how hereditary characteristics are transmitted.

It is a common belief that life depends on two vital factors—oxygen and sunlight. Therefore, it is something of a surprise to discover that there are present in the environment today organisms which are independent of both. Two examples are found among the sulphur bacteria which are able to synthesize all the metabolites, proteins, carbohydrates and fats of their cells directly from inorganic materials.[1] It is undoubtedly true that this group of enterprising micro-organisms represents very primitive forms of life; and yet by no stretch of the imagination could they be termed " simple organisms." They are, in fact,

[1] One non-sulphur organism, a methane producing bacterium, *may* be capable of this also, but it is not established.

more complicated than many more specialized bacteria. Nevertheless, their ability to survive without free oxygen or solar energy gives them a special place in our study.

We can be reasonably certain that when life first arose upon the earth, methane, ammonia and hydrogen were by far the largest concentrations of gases in the atmosphere, with little or no free oxygen. This atmosphere would, of course, be quite impossible for modern forms of life—but some of the sulphur bacteria would thrive and multiply quite readily.

Thus we know of at least two organisms capable of existing without oxygen or sunlight; indeed sulphate-reducing bacteria are often grown in a vacuum.[1] Like plants, these bacteria are able to build up their cell material from inorganic compounds, but whereas plants depend on solar energy in photosynthesis, these organisms obtain the necessary energy from the reduction of CO_2,[2] all of which is striking evidence of life's versatility.

Of further interest is the fact that certain blue-green algæ are themselves capable of oxidizing sulphur. They were, in fact, the first plants to appear on the pumic and volcanic ash after the eruption of Krakatoa; and since they are able to grow under conditions which would be quite impossible for more highly organized plant-life, they were sought by biologists and have been discovered living in hot springs at temperatures of 50 to 60 degrees C. as well as in the frozen lakes of Antarctica.

The secret of the blue-green algæ's amazing adaptability is that it does not conform to the cellular structure of ordinary plants, even of other algæ. According to Mr. G. E. Fogg,[3] lecturer in botany at University College, London, it has less in common with ordinary plants than plants have with animals. The individual cells are roughly hemispherical in shape, about 0·01 mm. in diameter, and are composed of granular protoplasm, a uniform bluish-green in colour, enclosed in a gelatinous sheath. They multiply by division.

In fact, writes Mr. Fogg, some blue-green algæ, if colourless, would be indistinguishable from certain bacteria, which strongly

1 "The Sulphur Bacteria," by John Postgate, *New Biology*, 17, (1954).
2 *Thiobacillus denitrificans* oxidizing S at the expense of NO_3 and *D. desulphurians* oxidizing H_2 at the expense of SO_4.
3 "Blue-green algae," by G. E. Fogg, *New Biology*, 5, (1948).

suggests that they were evolved before the distinction between plants and animals arose (see chart, Fig. 6). Although the comparison cannot be taken too far (e.g. some bacteria possess flagella), there appears little doubt that the two groups share a common ancestry.

Although bacteria do not contain chlorophyll, these tiny one-celled organisms belong to the plant world. There are three main groups: rod-shaped (bacilli), spherical (cocci) and spiral-like (spirilla). Some bacteria grow in long chains or mosaics, while the spirilla have hairs (flagella) which they lash to and fro to propel themselves through the fluid in which they occur (Fig. 26).

Bacteria reproduce by division; having reached a certain age they simply split in two instead of dying, each half beginning a new life of its own. Fast growing bacteria at body temperature divide every twenty to forty minutes, but the majority of non-pathogenic organisms grow much more slowly, dividing only once every few hours or even days.

One of the important functions of these minute organisms is that they break down and rebuild complex substances, some decomposing dead materials, others absorbing the nitrogen in the air and converting it into useful materials (e.g. nitrates in the soil). As we have seen, some bacteria are capable of building up their living tissue from raw chemicals, some being capable of doing this without any help from the sun—even in total darkness. Some forms are nourished on rocks which they literally eat and break down into soil; and on such chemical substances, they are able to live and multiply. We cannot be certain that at life's beginning they were actually present in these particular forms, but there are definite indications that something like them existed in pre-Cambrian times.

Another important characteristic of bacteria is that they can become quiescent in which state they are able to withstand enormous variations of temperature. They can survive temperatures of -190 degrees C. under laboratory conditions and, at the other extreme, immersion in boiling water for hours.

Whatever form life originally adopted, it is reasonable to assume that there were many variations of the basic type, just as there are many variations among the bacteria of the modern world. Crowther suggested [1] that the first organisms built up their living cells from raw chemicals, a process which he assumes absorbed all their energies and left nothing over for novel developments. But others, he said, might have shortened the chemical process by feeding on other organisms. This would have greatly simplified the process of digestion because half the work of building up the complicated substance of life would have been accomplished by the first organism. The second organism would, therefore, have excess energy with which to stimulate evolution, and among the first evolutionary tendencies would be movement in search of food (viz., the flagella, or moving hairs on the spirilli bacteria).

A vital factor in the evolutionary struggle was the development of chlorophyll. This enabled organisms to use sunlight to separate oxygen atoms from carbon dioxide and water, storing up the energy of hydrogen and carbon products in the form of carbohydrates—starch, cellulose, insulin, etc. This process of combining simple substances, water and carbon dioxide, into more complex chemical substances, under the influence of sunlight (photosynthesis) is the mechanism by which plants use energy to create living tissue. Once this stage had been reached, the development of plant-life and its evolution through microscopic algæ, lichens and seaweeds was assured.

Among the early organisms were those which did not develop chlorophyll. They multiplied at the expense of the plants and started another pathway of evolution which ultimately led to the animals (see chart, Fig. 17), a stage which could not have been reached before a primitive plant life had been well established, since animals are dependent on plants for food.

A remarkable little creature called the Euglena (Fig. 13), a single-cell organism which shares both plant and animal characteristics, appears to be close to this division in life's evolution. Its jelly-like body, which is broader at the front than at the back, consists of an outer layer of protoplasm. Near the centre of its interior is the nucleus, a denser substance composed of chromatin. This nucleus not only controls the creature's activities but is also responsible for the formation of new proto-

1 "An Outline of the Universe."

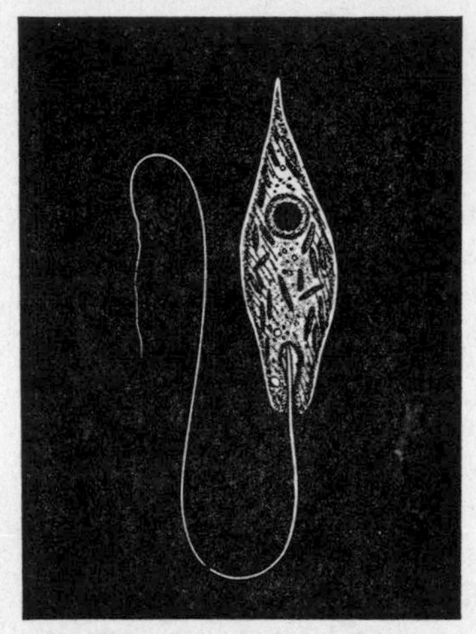

Fig. 13.

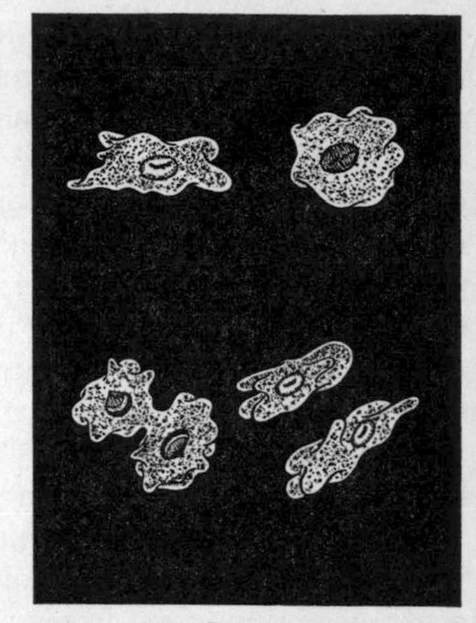

Fig. 14.

Fig. 13. Euglena, a remarkable single-celled organism which is part plant, part animal. *Plant characteristics:* presence of chlorophyll, absorbs organic solutions through its walls, builds up starch. *Animal characteristics:* presence of sensitive "eye-spot," contractile vacuole, ingests solid particles and has power of movement.

Fig. 14. Amœba, showing four stages in reproduction. For this tiny organism, there is no such thing as natural death.

plasm. A whip-like extension to the protoplasm enables the organism to pull itself through the water by a lashing movement of the flagella. The body is also constantly changing shape, elongating the protoplasm and following up with the rest of its mass.

Another interesting feature is a red "eye-spot" which is sensitive to light. But more remarkable still is the fact that this microscopic organism possesses a simple mouth and a contactile vacuole, which enables it to feed like an animal by washing down particles of food. On the other hand, like a plant, it is able to absorb carbon dioxide from water for the manufacture of starch; and by absorbing salts from the water, it also obtains nitrogen and other chemical elements. However, by growing several generations of Euglena in the dark, Lwoff was able to cause some of the progeny to lose their chlorophyll permanently. They were then indistinguishable from the protozoon Astasia, normally claimed by zoologists as an animal.

However, it is the amœba that is generally regarded as belonging to the lowest type of "first animals" and it is, in fact,

Fig. 15. The amœba, a unicellular organism belonging to the group known as " protozoa " (the first animals). Probably, it represents a stage in evolution beyond the primordial cell as great as that between itself and man.

much simpler in structure than the Euglena. It probably represents a stage in evolution beyond the primordial molecule as great as that between itself and man. Single-celled, it is a speck of living matter about one-hundredth of an inch across, virtually structureless, and consisting of a nucleus surmounted by jelly-like matter which is constantly changing shape.

In spite of its apparent simplicity, the amœba has some remarkable attributes. It can sense the presence of food, and will move towards it by thrusting out from its irregular jelly-like structure protrusions which form " false feet." It will then embrace the food particle with these " false feet," enclose it completely with its body, and absorb it. Having obtained the nourishment it needs, the organism simply unwraps itself and discards what remains of the food particle. The creature also has some kind of nervous system. If touched by a needle or irradiated with strong ultra-violet light, it will instantly contract into a globule of jelly. And yet, under the microscope all the amœba reveals by way of internal structure is a central nucleus, dark in colour and apparently enclosed in a cyst, and a transparent jelly-like outer body.

Perhaps most significant of all, however, is the similarity between amœba and the cells of higher animals. All living things are, of course, made up of a structure consisting of one or more units, or cells, which for a time at least, have an independent existence. One of life's great mysteries is the way these cells organize themselves and perpetuate the species. The human body, for example, is a mass of specialized cells, ranging from those which constitute flesh and blood to nerves and the "grey matter" of the brain. Fig. 12 shows in diagrammatic form an interesting comparison between the one-celled amœba and the multi-cellular structure of the higher animals.

The course evolution has taken to produce these more specialized forms is too well known to require elaboration here. Yet something may be said of the way in which evolution works.

Everything in nature is constantly changing. Nothing ever stands still. In the depths of space, galaxies are forming out of hydrogen gas; within the galaxies stars are being born in great profusion. Similarly, the principle of change is evident in all things that live and grow. The animals and plants of our world are all descendants of forms which have preceded them in time, and there is evidence that modifications in the descendants have occurred in parallel with changing surroundings. Moreover, this changing biological pattern appears in general to have tended towards a progressively higher level of organization, leading to the evolution of more complex organisms.

The fact of evolution cannot be seriously disputed and yet, a century after Darwin, its workings are still imperfectly understood.

The science of genetics, founded at the turn of the present century, provided the first substantial clues, explaining how the characteristics of plants and animals are handed on through continuous generations. The key to the problem emerged from intimate studies of the structure of cells, made possible by improvements in microscope techniques. The cells of the human body, which have a diameter of about ·0005 in., each contain a nucleus surrounded by protoplasm and an enclosing wall of outer membrane. Within the nucleus is a mass of tangled skein-like structures called chromosomes, the number of which differs from creature to creature. The fruit fly, for example, carries within its cells eight chromosomes, human beings forty-eight and some crayfish as many as 200.

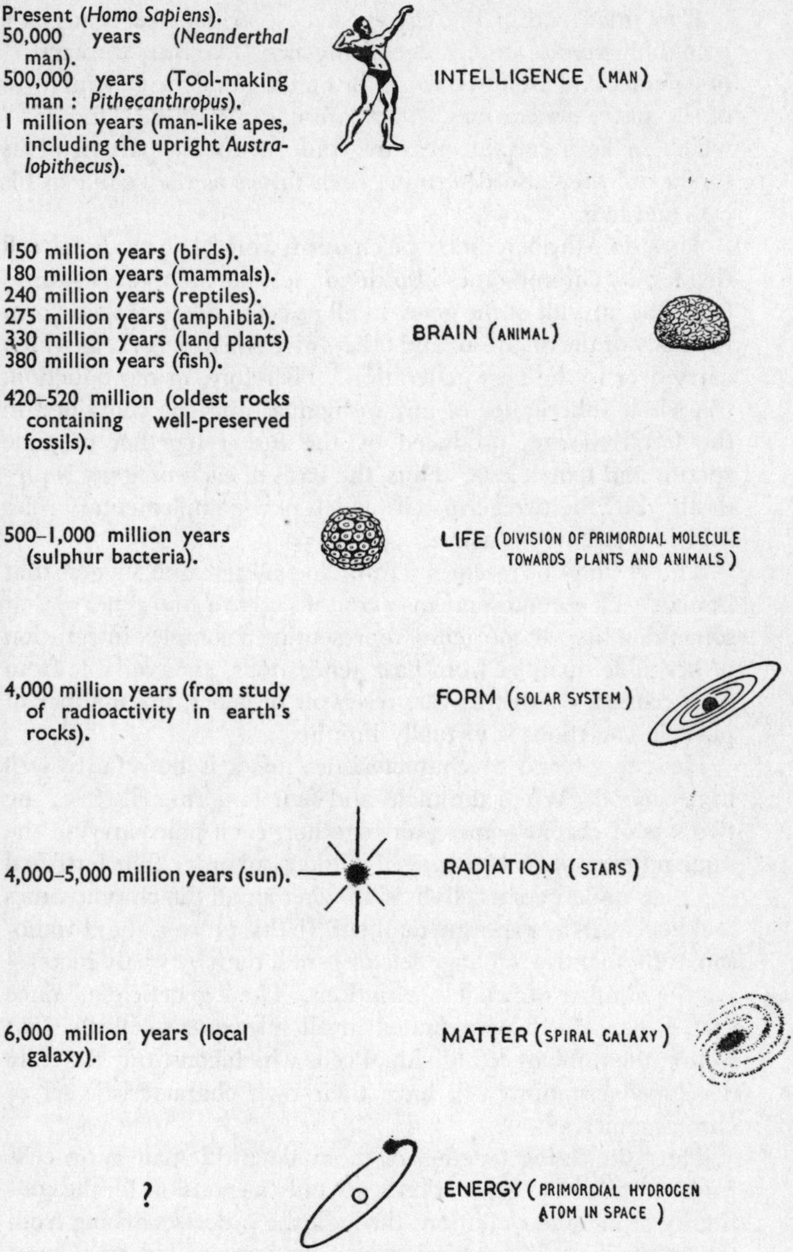

Present (*Homo Sapiens*).
50,000 years (*Neanderthal* man).
500,000 years (Tool-making man : *Pithecanthropus*).
1 million years (man-like apes, including the upright *Australopithecus*).

INTELLIGENCE (MAN)

150 million years (birds).
180 million years (mammals).
240 million years (reptiles).
275 million years (amphibia).
330 million years (land plants)
380 million years (fish).

BRAIN (ANIMAL)

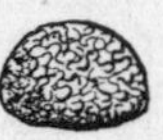

420–520 million (oldest rocks containing well-preserved fossils).

500–1,000 million years (sulphur bacteria).

LIFE (DIVISION OF PRIMORDIAL MOLECULE TOWARDS PLANTS AND ANIMALS)

4,000 million years (from study of radioactivity in earth's rocks).

FORM (SOLAR SYSTEM)

4,000–5,000 million years (sun).

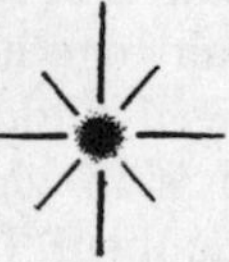

RADIATION (STARS)

6,000 million years (local galaxy).

MATTER (SPIRAL GALAXY)

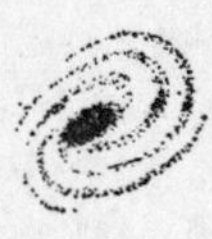

?

ENERGY (PRIMORDIAL HYDROGEN ATOM IN SPACE)

Fig. 16. The evolutionary sequence according to our experience.

Contained within the chromosomes, strung like beads, are incredibly minute structures called genes. These are the carriers of heredity and are responsible for maintaining the general form of successive generations. They are nature's subtle " moulds," which make a certain creature conform to the pattern of its forebears; they also determine such things as the colour of his eyes and hair.

How does the hereditary mechanism work? When a living cell divides, its chromosomes also divide so that the total organism bears the imprint of the genes in all its cells. Some of these form the body of the organism and others give rise to germ cells which carry over to the next generation. Therefore, in reproduction, the whole inheritance of any individual must be contained in the fertilized egg, produced by the fusing together of male sperms and female ova. Thus, the basis of each progeny is predestined by the two germ cells which play complementary rôles in the hereditary influence.

The findings of recent micro-biological research suggest that in man each chromosome may contain up to 1,000 genes so that something like 48,000 genes, representing a complex integration of heritable qualities from past generations, are available from each parent. With this vast reservoir of genes, the number of possible variations is virtually infinite.

How this blend of characteristics arises is now fairly well understoood. When the male and female germ cells fuse, the two sets of chromosomes pair together, each pair carrying the same number of genes arranged in identical order. The fertilized egg then undergoes a cell division wherein all the chromosomes and hence all the genes are doubled. In this process, the chromosomes frequently exchange sets of genes, thereby vastly increasing the number of possible variations. The " genetic die," once cast, is henceforth perpetuated in all subsequent cell divisions so that the millions of individual cells which constitute the fully developed organism will have their own characteristic set of chromosomes.

Thus, the fusing together of the male and female germ cells from generation to generation is not only responsible for the continuity of life and evolution; through the processes arising from the intermixing of parental genes, changes are brought about

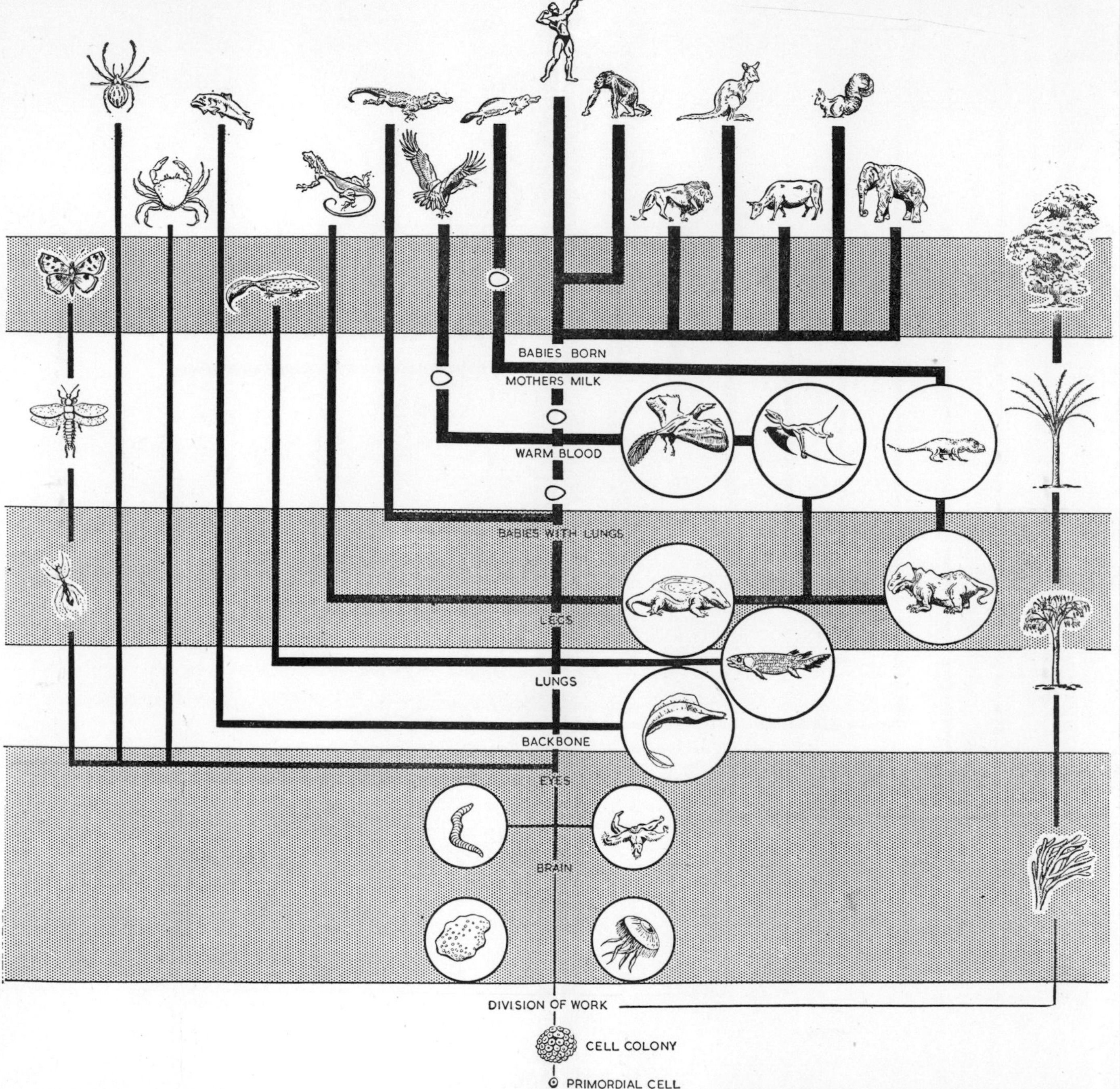

Fig. 17. Chart of evolution. (The pictorial subjects represent the *trend* of evolution only—not a direct evolutionary sequence).

CHART OF EVOLUTION

Starting with the primordial cell, this diagram outlines the general trend evolution has taken—first the single cell, then colonies of cells which led to a multitude of different forms, in one direction to the plants and in the other to creatures with nervous systems, segmented bodies, eyes and, eventually, backbones. From life's beginnings in the sea the evolution of lungs and legs enabled certain forms to enlarge their experience on land and, by laying eggs containing food and water, they were able to rear their young independently of the sea. Many species died out in an unequal struggle against the environment. But in the fullness of time, warm blood gave birds and mammals a degree of independence from changes in climate which strengthened their capacity to survive. It is remarkable that many features of evolution are re-enacted in the development of each new human being (e.g. beginning of life as a single cell; embryo passes through a stage when gill arches appear in the neck region similar to those which, in fish, lead to the development of functional gills ; vestige of a third eyelid, functional in birds and rabbits, in the inner corner of the eye ; existence at the base of the pelvis of nodules of bone, the caudal vertebræ, suggesting a link with tailed ancestors).

from generation to generation which ensure that while a general continuity is maintained the offspring are never perfect copies of a parent. It also explains why offspring of the same parents (with the exception of identical twins) are never perfect copies of each other.

Yet another genetic process responsible for introducing new characteristics has special significance in evolution. This process, called *mutation*, results in a gene undergoing a chemical change causing it to induce unusual effects, which in some cases may even be harmful. It appears that all creatures carry such mutant genes, and those which produce very marked changes are on the whole more detrimental than those which produce only slight changes. The latter are believed to be responsible for evolutionary progress, so that when a change in the surroundings makes a particular mutation advantageous, a creature will profit from it. In this way it acquires an advantage over its contemporaries which enhances its ability to survive.

Evolution, then, according to present biological concepts, is the result of natural selection and random variations. Thus, in the classic example of the transition of fish to amphibia, it would be true to say that fish with leg-like fins and lung-like organs would tend to survive by virtue of them, while others either died out or survived because of different variations. Hence, only those variations that enabled their possessors to survive in competition with their less favoured companions persisted, while other variations which were numerically the majority, died out with the creatures possessing them. Similarly, lungs evolved because, once creatures had reached a certain complexity by other evolutionary steps, conditions existed in which a variant able to stay out of water a long time would have an advantage (e.g. in food supply) over his fellows. Sooner or later, among many variations of all kinds, the right one turned up and a creature something like an amphibian found a brave new world awaiting him—only to be superseded sooner or later by a less aquatic, more terrestrial variant of himself.

This is the picture presented by contemporary biological science, which leaves little room for the old idea that changes in environment in themselves are responsible for producing effects that are heritable; so that only those environmental factors that affect the germ cells directly, such as irradiation, are relevant. Neither does it seem possible that techniques acquired by an organism during its lifetime can be passed on to succeeding generations. For example, even if for some reason a fish tried to walk on its fins, and even if it became quite accomplished in this art, its ability would in no way affect the genetic composition of its sperms or ova; it would not be inherited.

This much is clear—but is it the complete picture? Can natural selection arising from the shuffling of genes between partners, and random variations resulting from mutations account for the degree of organization revealed in evolution? Moreover, can it explain the orderly upward climb of the organic world, with its progressively higher levels of organization? A person lacking the specialized knowledge of the biologist would be forgiven if, from the standpoint of observation, he regarded this process as expressing order, not disorder.

CHAPTER THREE *Our Neighbour Worlds*

> *" We know the prodigality of Nature. How many acorns are scattered for one that grows to an oak? And need she be more careful of her stars than of her acorns? "*
>
> SIR ARTHUR EDDINGTON
> " The Nature of the Physical World."

WHAT OF life on other worlds? The first difficulty we encounter is that no one has yet invented a simple but satisfactory definition of " life." Neither do we understand what conditions are necessary to bring it into being; thus, until astronomers are agreed upon the question of how the solar system arose, any discussion of life outside this earth must remain somewhat academic. However, with these reservations in mind, we can embark on a tentative exploration.

What is certain is that any kind of life we know must depend on chemical action for its energy supply, and what is more, chemical action involving the development of rather complex molecules. What, apparently, places a limit on living things having a chemical structure, is temperature. Consequently, life on the surface of a star, at a temperature of several thousands of degrees, would be impossible because only the simplest of molecules could exist under those conditions. Life in the vast interstellar void would be equally improbable. The conclusion is inevitable, that life is possible only on the surface of a planet which is irradiated by its parent sun.

The distance of the planet from its sun is clearly one of the chief factors. The " zone of habitation " about any star has been defined as that region where surface temperatures are roughly between the boiling and freezing points of water, and in our own system it is found that such conditions prevail from the orbit of Venus to the orbit of Mars. In this zone it is probable that any planet of suitable size and composition could support life of one kind or another. The earth, situated between these two planets, appears to be close to the ideal relationship, although living forms might well exist elsewhere under conditions which are quite unlike those in our own experience. Mars is an example of a planet, colder than our own, in which short "living seasons" might occur suitable for some of the simpler terrestrial life forms, especially those which could lie dormant during the more rigorous periods. We have seen that life is highly adaptable. Simple forms of plant life can live in hot springs at temperatures as high as 160 degrees F. and bacteria spores can survive in very cold storage for years.

If we could approach Mars in a spaceship, we should see that large parts of its surface have an ochre colouring; these are great arid deserts which have given that intriguing world the name of the "Red Planet." There are also brilliant white polar caps, superficially resembling those of the earth, which glisten in the sunlight. And here and there, on the light-coloured desert, are darker areas which appear prominently in the southern hemisphere.

On the maps of Mars which astronomers prepared in the mid-nineteenth century, the famous dark areas are labelled "seas" and the vast ochre-coloured tracts, "continents." At the time, there was even a suggestion that the "dry land" was covered with some kind of orange vegetation. Today, although the Red Planet still retains much of its mystery, we know that, far from being oceans on Mars, there is almost a complete dearth of water. The light-coloured regions are, in fact, immense arid deserts—and what is more, deserts of a rather unfamiliar kind.

It would be most improbable that they are composed of sand, like the Sahara, for sand can only result from the soiling of igneous rocks by running water. Although our knowledge is limited, it appears unlikely that Mars ever possessed the great fluid oceans necessary to account for such enormous deposits. An alternative theory suggests that the dark areas may be ancient sea beds where vegetation still clings to a perilous existence.

There is, of course, not a scrap of evidence to support this theory. If shallow seas ever existed on Mars, they are certainly not there today and the most one can say is that, if life *did*

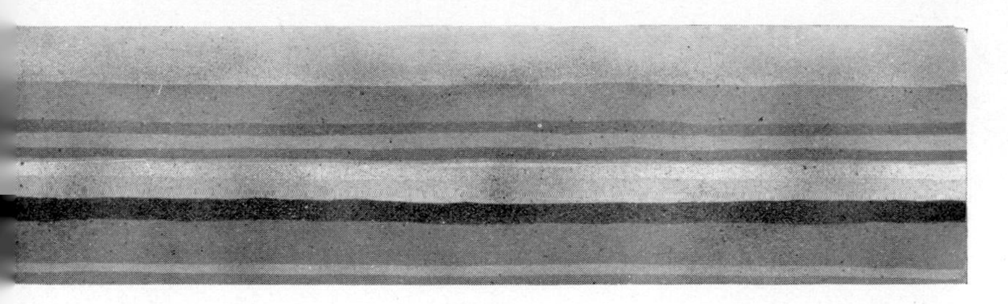

18. *In prehistoric times when shallow seas covered the present great land masses, many ts of the sea-bed were flat, consisting of layer upon layer of sedimentary particles, resulting n the wearing down of the igneous rocks by rain, heat, frost and wind. As the material accumu- s, it gradually compacts and hardens, the muds turning into clays and shales, the sand into dstones. With the coming of life in the sea, other sedimentary particles—those of decaying life itself—produced new layers of the earth's crust, the limestones.*

Fig. 19. *Great earth movements caused the crust to be pushed along in folds.*

. 20. *Folds of rock weathered by the elements became mountains, explaining why fossil nains of creatures which once inhabited primitive seas, are sometimes found on the slopes of mountains.*

Fig. 21. As the rains of centuries subside, the earth's stormy atmosphere settles down to allow a new warmth to bathe the infant planet—the warmth of the Sun. Silently, unseen, in shallow waters, a new revolution leads to the emergence of the first living molecules. And, in the

begin to evolve under such conditions, it probably would not have had sufficient time in which to turn into more advanced forms.

What gives the light regions their characteristic hue is naturally a matter for speculation. One theory suggests that the surface redness may be due to the presence of metallic oxides, possibly iron oxide, in which case the oxygen astronomers seek in the Martian environment might still be there locked up in the great ochre deserts. The nearest approach to such conditions on the earth are the famous " Painted Deserts " of Arizona. Audouin Dollfus thinks it likely that the surface is coated with irregular deposits of another oxygen and iron compound, limonite, spread about in a pulverized condition, while more recent studies by Dr. Gerhard Kuiper suggest that the covering may be a brownish igneous rock known as felsite, a silicate of aluminium and potassium. Again, it is a question much more of speculation than of factual evidence which, however, is scarcely surprising when it is remembered that Mars is at least 150 times further away than the moon.

A comparatively small planet, Mars has a mean diameter of 4,250 miles and a surface gravity only 38 per cent of our own; there a man weighing 200 lb. on our own planet would weigh the equivalent of only 76 lb. This weaker gravitation also means that falling objects would descend more slowly, with a rate of acceleration of 12 ft. per second every second, as compared with the earth's 32 ft. per second per second, so that an athlete who can jump 24 ft. on the earth could theoretically clear 72 ft. on Mars.

The Martian day is only forty-one minutes longer than our own, but its year (the period the planet takes to travel once round the sun) is almost double—687 earth-days. Consequently, the Martian seasons last approximately twice as long as ours do.

The earth's atmosphere is largely composed of nitrogen and oxygen; that of Mars may well be made up chiefly of nitrogen. Some carbon dioxide has been detected, and there is probably a little argon. At present, no trace of oxygen has been found, although water vapour presumably exists in minute quantities. Whereas the earth's atmosphere extends more than 300 miles, it is probable that the Martian atmosphere is little more than sixty miles deep, and because of the weak gravitation, it is impossible for the planet to retain light gases such as hydrogen and helium. For the same reason, the density of the atmosphere does not fall off anything like so sharply as it does on the earth; in fact, according to some astronomers, clouds have been observed at altitudes as great as twenty miles.

Temperatures on the planet are extreme, ranging from −95 degrees F. at night to almost 80 degrees F. at noon in the tropical belt. The coldest temperature ever recorded under natural conditions on the earth is −96 degrees F.[1] (at Yerkhoyansk, a Siberian village, in 1892) and the hottest temperature, 136 degrees F. (at Tripoli, in 1922). However, on Mars, there is no gradual warming up or cooling down over periods of months, as occurs on our own planet; wide extremes of temperature occur every day within the space of a few hours.

That life of some kind exists on Mars, despite the rigorous conditions, can no longer be seriously doubted. The dark areas have mystified astronomers for many years, but recent observations have strengthened the view that they consist of vegetation which can survive in the oxygen-poor atmosphere.

In 1954, when Mars closed in to 39,800,000 miles, Dr. E. C. Slipher of the Lowell Observatory, Arizona, and a team of observers went to the Lamont-Hussey Observatory, Bloemfontein, South Africa, where the viewing conditions are exceptionally good and took more than 20,000 photographs with the intention of recording any changes that took place on the planet's surface during five months of continuous observation. The chosen period made it possible to record the recession of the Martian winter and the shrinking of the vast polar caps.

The polar caps of Mars were first discovered in 1666 by G. D. Cassini, who believed them to be composed of snow after the fashion of the earth's polar mantles. Earlier this century, the idea was widespread that they were made up of carbon dioxide—" dry ice "—and it was only in 1948, when Kuiper made spectroscopic investigations of the planet at the McDonald Observatory, in Texas, that Cassini's original theory was finally verified; the Martian polar caps are, in fact, some

[1] In May, 1957, an American I.G.Y. expedition, encamped at the South Pole, recorded a temperature of −104.4 degrees F.

frosty, or snowy deposit. Nevertheless, they are quite different from the frozen wastes of Antarctica, where the ice is of considerable depth. We know from observation that the Martian caps melt very rapidly with the onset of warmer conditions and therefore must be extremely thin, certainly no more than a few inches. In the long bitter winter, the southern cap may cover an area of over four million square miles, but in summer, the ice retreats to a small patch; in 1894, it actually disappeared altogether for a brief period. Despite the fact that the northern cap is not subject to such wide temperature extremes, it too can cover a vast area in the depths of the northern winter, whereas in the Martian summer it is difficult to pick out even with the aid of a telescope of some power.

With the melting of the polar caps, a darker coloration occurs at the fringe of the retreating white areas, exactly as though ice were melting and watering the desert. At first, this was believed to be an optical illusion resulting from the contrast of colour between the polar cap and the desert, but investigations by Kuiper have shown that the phenomenon is real. One suggestion is that it is the result of moisture dampening the ground.

Perhaps it is not quite true to describe the polar caps as "melting," for under the conditions of pressure and temperature prevailing on Mars, it may be possible for a solid substance to "sublime," passing directly from the solid into the gaseous state without becoming liquid at all. This is not to suggest that sublimation is the main mechanism in the shrinking of the polar caps, though it is almost certain to play a part.

Another interesting point is that when the Martian polar caps eventually begin to shrink, they do not recede evenly. For a short time, small whitish areas are left behind, suggesting that the ground is elevated in these regions, while rifts are sometimes observed within the mantle itself which probably mark the location of Martian valleys. The onset of winter is accompanied by the appearance of a whitish overlying haze in the polar regions, which is presumably responsible for the deposit.

It is in the Martian spring that changes occur on the planet's surface which seems to indicate the presence of something that lives and grows. As the polar caps recede, dark areas begin to spread from pole to equator, suggesting some kind of vegetation. The dark areas are more prominent in the southern hemisphere, possibly due to the relatively greater amount of moisture released from the southern polar cap.

The Slipher expedition of 1954 revealed that important changes have taken place in these dark areas since similar observations were made in 1907, 1924 and 1939; their photographs clearly show dark areas which were not previously recorded.

What are these dark regions? Vegetation seems the only logical answer. If they were not composed of living matter capable of reproducing itself, they would long ago have been covered over by dust blown up from the ochre deserts. This is more than a theory. Martian dust storms have actually been observed by astronomers. Moreover, the areas in question undergo definite colour changes—from light green to dark green in the Martian spring to yellow or gold in summer, and to brown in autumn. Yet this seasonal revival does not begin in the tropic zone but spreads from the polar regions, which as we have seen strongly suggests that it is linked with the gradual spread of moisture from the melting ice cap.

One should emphasize, however, that not all astronomers are convinced that the dark areas *are* vegetation. For example, D. B. McLaughlin of the University of Michigan Observatory suggests that the dark areas might consist of ash thrown up into the atmosphere by volcanoes and spread over the deserts by winds. The shapes of many of the dark areas, he says, have a strange way of repeating themselves around the Martian globe in a parallel formation, elongated in the direction of probable winds. According to estimates, winds of at least 25 m.p.h. sometimes blow in the desert regions.

McLaughlin suggests that when exposed to the Martian atmosphere, common types of volcanic ash would weather to a soil in which green chlorite and epidote would be abundant and that in powdery form this material would darken with moisture. Colour changes may be the result of chemical reactions which arise between the volcanic ash and salts and minerals in the soil. A certain amount of moisture to assist this process might even come from the volcanoes themselves.

To account for those surface features which do not correspond to the wind direction, it is suggested that these markings (particularly the so-called canals) may consist of lines of small volcanoes situated along major crustal fractures. Most of the canals, according to this theory, would be accounted for by ash deposited in roughly straight lines between the volcanoes, thus giving the illusion of continuity.

On the whole, this explanation of the Martian dark areas appears a good deal less plausible than the one involving vegetation. For one thing, there is as yet no evidence of volcanic activity on Mars, and certainly none that would account for deposits over so vast an area. Furthermore, to fit in with observational evidence, the volcanic activity would have to follow a seasonal cycle, for otherwise dust blown from the deserts would be continually covering over the ash and restoring the surface to a uniform ochre colouring. It also appears reasonable to assume that in summer water does not reach the dark areas across land but is carried as moisture in the atmosphere, circulated by the Martian winds. In fact, it appears that a good deal of water is exchanged in this way between the southern and northern polar caps. Therefore, it might be argued with equal conviction that any uniformity in the distribution and shape of the dark areas is due to vegetation which has been favourably served by moist air currents.

When photographs are taken of the planets in conjunction with a powerful telescope, the astronomer finds that coloured filters are as invaluable to him as they are to the enthusiastic photographer. A photograph of Mars taken through a blue filter reveals only the top of the atmosphere, because blue light being of short wave-length, has little penetrative power. Consequently, when astronomers wish to record peculiarities in the planet's atmosphere, blue or sometimes violet filters are used. When, however, it is desired to record surface detail (the distribution of the dark areas, for example), the astronomer uses a red filter which enables him to penetrate right to the planet's surface, just as an orange fog-light penetrates terrestrial fog. Comparison of photographs of Mars taken in red and blue light (Figs. 41 and 42) shows this effect very plainly.

When Mars is photographed in blue light, the clouds recorded appear to be of three main types—predominant obscuring yellow clouds, which are thought to be associated with dust storms or, less probably, fine ash ejected into the atmosphere by volcanoes; " white " clouds which occur at a greater altitude and which can sometimes obscure surface features beneath them, and finally, the high-level " blue clouds," which are so-named because they appear most prominently when photographed in blue light. However, whether these latter features can be properly regarded as clouds is, at present, open to conjecture; some observers prefer to regard them merely as haze.

Fortunately, the telescope is not the only instrument that can be used to investigate the planets. When sunlight is reflected from planets and analysed in the spectroscope, it reveals something of the elements which are present on its surface. Professor G. A. Tikhoff of Russia claims that the spectrum of the dark areas of Mars does, in fact, show evidence of chlorophyll, the green colouring matter of plants. These plants, he suggests, adapt themselves to the cold conditions by absorbing the warming red and yellow solar rays and reflect blue and green, which agrees very well with the colours we actually observe. Professor Tikhoff points out that the absorption of plants which exist under rigorous conditions on the earth varies to some extent with altitude.

Fir trees show dark in infra-red photographs because of the resin in their leaves which protects them from the rigorous arctic conditions in which some of them live. This does not mean that fir trees grow on Mars, but it could mean that Martian plants protect themselves from the cold with a similar substance which absorbs the infra-red radiation from the chlorophyll and thus helps to retain some warmth.

Independent investigations by Dr. Kuiper in the United States contrast the spectrum of higher plants with the spectrum of lichens. Higher plants reflect strongly in a wave-band when red joins infra-red, whereas lichens reflect very little through those zones.[1]

[1] " The Colours of Martian Vegetation," by Dr. A. E. Slater. *Spaceflight,* Vol. 1, No. 1, October 1956, pp. 35-9.

Dr. Kuiper points out that the spectrum of the Martian dark areas resembles that of lichens in these wave-lengths, but that it should not be taken to mean that the Martian spectrum is " characteristic " of lichens; merely that it is " not incompatible " with the existence of lichens.

To test this possibility, attempts are being made in America to reproduce the chemical and physical conditions on Mars in the laboratory, with the intention of determining whether or not lichens can be induced to grow. A similar line of research is being pursued in Russia.

A lichen is a mixture of two quite different forms of life; a fungus and an alga. The alga is of the single cell kind whose microscopic cells tangle with the threads of fungus and contain chlorophyll which enables them to build up the substances needed for growth. The fungus helps itself to these substances and appears to get the best of the bargain. It is clear, therefore, that lichens are not among the most elementary forms of life; and in spite of what has already been said, this fact must detract somewhat from the many arguments in favour of something similar to lichens being found on Mars.

A similar argument could be used against the chances of chlorophyll being present on Mars; it is quite a complicated substance. Its molecule consists of some 125 atoms, of which one is magnesium, four are nitrogen, five oxygen, and the rest carbon and hydrogen; the main pattern of their arrangement is a circle of pentagonal rings with a long chain attached at one point. Could not some quite different type of coloured pigment have evolved on the Red Planet?

All this, of course, is highly speculative. It is quite possible that the Martian vegetation does not resemble lichens at all, but is of a type which is quite distinctive. Indeed, it would be evidence of a remarkable uniformity in nature if earth-type vegetation had occurred on Mars. One of the things we must not overlook is that the circumstances which brought life into existence on the earth are peculiar to the earth and that quite different forms of life may exist elsewhere in the universe. We anxiously probe the other planets of our solar system for evidence of atmospheres containing oxygen—and find none with the particular blend of gases capable of supporting our kind of life.

What we tend to overlook is the fact that life has not emerged because the earth happens to have the right gases to support it; it is becoming abundantly clear that life has adapted itself to the chemical materials that happened to be present. It has already been pointed out that the earth's present oxygen-rich atmosphere is the result of vegetation transforming an earlier atmosphere. When life first arose upon the earth, probably the most abundant gases were ammonia and methane, both of which would be highly poisonous to all modern forms of life. Thus life may not be the rare and accidental event that some biologists have pictured it to be, but something quite fundamental in the universe.

We may find, therefore, that all the Martian plant-life has in common with lichens or other hardy earth-type vegetation is the ability to grow under rigorous conditions.

It should not be overlooked that green plants, in common with animals, require atmospheric oxygen to break down food material in order to provide energy for growth, reproduction, repair and general metabolism. At the same time, there is an independent system for synthesizing sugars using carbon dioxide from the atmosphere and water from the soil. The energy needed for this comes from the sun. The second cycle reacts much more rapidly than the respiratory cycle and the plant gives out more oxygen than it absorbs. The oxygen released is obtained from the water.

In his book, "The Red and Green Planet," Dr. Hubertus Strughold of the Department of Space Medicine in the United States, stresses the need for water "as a prerequisite for active life." It is a sobering thought that were there no plants to split the water molecule, there could be no oxygen in our atmosphere.

One of the key features of Strughold's interesting book is the suggestion that Martian vegetation may keep within its tissues the oxygen it produces by photosynthesis and then uses this oxygen for respiration, instead of taking it from the air, as earthly plants are able to do. On Mars, because of the limited amount of water available and the reduced solar energy, plants would be able to produce very little oxygen beyond their own needs, and therefore Martian vegetation would not be capable

of enriching the atmosphere as ours do. Therefore, assuming that life has evolved on similar lines as on earth, the only types of organism that could possibly survive would be lichen and bacteria.

There is, however, absolutely no reason why enzymic and energy transfer systems could not have arisen on Mars which are fully adapted to the rigorous conditions prevailing there, so that it is not impossible that more complex biological systems might exist. Although the parallel should not be taken too far, there are on the earth certain organisms which indicate nature's versatility in the face of difficult conditions. For example, certain desert animals have been found to give out more water than they take in, implying that they manufacture some of it chemically within their bodies.

In his book, "Man and the Planets,"[1] Dr. Robert S. Richardson (in conjunction with F. B. Salisbury [2]) has suggested a biochemistry with possible application to Mars, in which nitrogen replaces oxygen in the energy relations of the organism. In this hypothetical system, nitrogen is oxidized through ammonia to nitrate. This kind of reaction, he says, might be adapted to the complex chemistry of carbon. A transfer of energy would still be applicable, since there is ample carbon in the Martian atmosphere. Photosynthesis could still play its part but might involve red and blue absorbing pigments, having the same appearance as chlorophyll in visible light. This might concern, in addition to the formation of carbon skeletons, the direct formation of carbon-nitrogen bonds, amounting to a photosynthetic nitrogen-fixation. The medium of reaction might still be water, or it might be some other compound which remained liquid at much lower temperatures; it might even be synthesized by the plants themselves.

Again, these remarks must be taken with reserve, for lacking wide biochemical experience we can only resort to guesswork. All that one can say with conviction is that such things do not seem impossible and, indeed, one might equally postulate a

[1] Published in the United States under the title "Exploring Mars."
[2] Graduate student in biology, California Institute of Technology, January 1954.

biochemistry in which oxygen is replaced by sulphur. We saw in Chapter Two that certain anaerobic bacteria, which almost certainly evolved when there was little or no oxygen in the earth's atmosphere (perhaps more than 800 million years ago), use sulphur instead of oxygen for their energy-relations and consequently can exist quite happily without air. This is a striking instance of the way in which life is capable of adapting itself, and if such things are possible on our own planet, there seems no reason why Mars, at least, should not possess organisms whose biochemistry is unique to the environment. In fact, Sir Harold Spencer Jones, the former Astronomer Royal, in his book, " Life on Other Worlds," has gone one better and considered a special kind of " high-temperature " life in which the basic life-building element is sodium.

It is one of those questions that will ultimately be resolved only through physical exploration. However, in the absence of evidence to the contrary, the possibility that other biochemistries may have arisen remains an intriguing thought. Extra-terrestrial life would then no longer be regarded merely as lichens and bacteria existing in some evolutionary blind-alley, but as systems of life which, like our own, show progressively higher levels of organization. On this basis, intelligent life would not be excluded.

No book dealing with the Red Planet would be complete without mention of the famous canals. Giovanni Schiaparelli, of Milan, who first drew attention to these strange markings in 1877, called them *canali*, which is Italian for " channels."

On the maps Schiaparelli drew of Mars, there was something else beyond the polar caps, the ochre deserts and the dark areas, which apparently no one had noticed before.[1] What they were is best explained by the following extract from his own notes: " All the vast extent of the Continents is furrowed upon every side by a network of numerous lines of a more or less pro-

[1] Mädler had, in fact, noticed markings, but nobody paid any attention to him, for as Schiaparelli saw them they were much narrower and straighter.

ounced dark colour . . . They traverse the planet for long listances in regular lines that do not at all resemble the winding courses of our streams. Some of the shorter ones do not attain 300 miles; others extend for many thousands . . . Some are easy to see; others are extremely difficult, and resemble the inest thread of a spider's web drawn across the disk." Although he canali were not observed by anyone else for some years, Schiaparelli not only recorded more mysterious lines in 1879 and 1881 but also reported that some of them ran in pairs.

When, at length, other astronomers began seeing canals, the whole question became the subject of a great controversy. Many observers were convinced that the canals were evidence of intelligent life, believing that what they saw were great irrigation systems which the Martians had constructed in a last desperate bid to preserve the resources of their "dying planet." On the other hand, there were the sceptics who believed that the markings were nothing more than an illusion resulting from the tendency of the human eye to join up spots and streaks into hard lines. You can test this theory for yourself by drawing a series of dots and dashes in a rough line on a piece of paper and looking at them from a distance through half-closed eyes. This, incidentally, is rather a good way of appreciating the conditions under which Mars is actually observed, for the earth's unsteady atmosphere diminishes the quality of our "seeing" and prevents us from picking out the more delicate surface markings. This difficulty particularly applies to photography. An object like Mars requires a long time exposure, which means that all the while the lens aperture is open, the atmosphere is steadily mussing the picture, erasing from it all the fine detail. This is the reason why the 200-inch telescope, despite its superior light-gathering power, is little improvement on quite modest instruments for planetary photography.

What a revolutionary boon the artificial satellite will be to astronomers of the future is not difficult to imagine. When we look at the planets through the ocean of air above us, they appear to "twinkle," an effect which is entirely due to the atmosphere. If instead we could make our observations from space, we should find that the planets (which, of course, shine by reflected sunlight) are precise discs of light.

Thus, our observations of the Red Planet are seriousl hampered by the earth's atmospheric envelope, and the use c telescopes of greater magnification only serves to enlarge i effects. The ultimate answer is to establish observatories i space stations [1] outside the earth, but until this can be done, th best results will be those obtained from observatories such as th Pic du Midi, situated high up in the Pyrénées. At this moun tain observatory, Dr. Audouin Dollfus has made a special stud of Mars, with particular attention to the " canals." He report that under normal seeing conditions, the markings appear har and sharp, extending mile upon mile as straight unbroken lines On the other hand, under conditions of optimum seeing, whe our atmosphere is unusually clear and steady, these lines appea to break down into irregular markings, rather like the dots an dashes on the paper. It must be said, however, that this has no been generally confirmed by other astronomers. When Dr Slipher made his observations of the planet in South Africa i 1954, he found striking evidence of the existence of these lines one of which he estimated extends in a perfectly straight line fo fully 1,500 miles. Another curious feature is that some of th lines actually run through each other, which is hardly what on would expect of a waterway of natural formation.

While controversy still reigns over the precise nature of the Martian " canals," there is one issue which appears conclusive. It is that the markings take part in the seasonal cycle; in the spring and summer, they appear darker, just as the blue-green regions do, which appears to link them with the Martian vegetation. Slipher himself has suggested that they resemble lines of vegetation along water-courses.

One of the great objections to the theory that these markings were artificial constructions was that, for us to observe them at all, they would have to be many miles in width. In fact, astronomers have estimated that some of the lines must be fully *twenty-five miles* wide. It was then suggested that what we actually saw was the spread of vegetation on the fertile land bordering the irrigation channels, such as a picture of the Nile delta might appear if taken from a great height.

[1] Strange, is it not, that the new Astronomer Royal, Professor Richard Van der Riet Woolley, should have described space travel in such scientifically precise and colourfully eloquent terms as " utter bilge."

When high-definition photographs of Mars can be taken, it ıay be found that the vegetation is associated with natural regular markings, though why they should extend in more or ss regular formation over such enormous distances few people re prepared to speculate.

Meanwhile, a little information has become available as the esult of observations made during the 1956 opposition when ne Red Planet passed closer to the earth than at any time since 924, to within 35,170,000 miles. It will not come so close gain until 1971.

Astronomers had looked upon the event with eager anticipa-on, but as it turned out, viewing conditions generally were ır from ideal. In Europe, the earth's weather was as trouble-ome as it generally is on big astronomical occasions, but fortu-ately observers in Africa, the United States and Japan were etter served by the elements. However, what few astronomers ad bargained for was unfavourable conditions on *Mars*. Wide-pread " haze " of unusual density in the Martian atmosphere bscured large areas of the planet's surface and although the ark areas could be distinguished they were unusually light in one.

The poor visibility is believed to have been the result of an normous dust storm, estimated to be fully 3,000 miles long and 50 miles wide, which had sprung up from the deserts. Accord-ng to Dr. Gerhard Kuiper, who made his observations at the McDonald Observatory, Texas, the storm was followed almost mmediately by what he described as a " summer blizzard." The polar caps had already begun to shrink considerably in the eriod between July and mid-August but on September 5, vhile the Martian summer was still young, a large whitish loud 800 miles wide formed over the pole. Nine days later it vas gone, leaving in its place a fresh snowy deposit. To account or this, Kuiper suggests that the dust storm which reached its eight in the late August lowered the surface temperature below ts summer average of 65 degrees F.

Dr. E. C. Slipher, observed Mars from Bloemfontein, in outh Africa, where he spent six months with the National Geographical Society's Mars Expedition, with the primary bject of photographing the canals. Of the 40,000 photographs

taken during this period, approximately 1,500 were obtaine
on his behalf by Mr. B. V. Somes-Charlton using what is know
as an " electronic telescope," developed by Pye, Ltd., of Cam
bridge. In essentials, this is simply a combination of a norma
astronomical telescope and a television camera with a photographic attachment. The great advantage of the device is tha
it makes possible a bigger and brighter image than is normall
obtainable, enabling exposure times to be shortened and thereb
reducing troublesome distortions due to the earth's unstead
atmosphere.

At the same time, the 60-inch and 100-inch telescopes o
Mount Wilson, in California, were trained on Mars; they had
in fact, been made available for thirty-six nights from May 5
to December 16, and of these, twenty-one nights were fron
August 10 to September 13, at the height of the opposition.

Test exposures of Mars were taken during the morning o
June 3 under very favourable conditions. " This morning,"
writes Dr. Robert S. Richardson, under whose directions th
observations were made, " the disc had a peculiar aspect which
I had not noticed before. There were innumerable irregula
blue lines extending across the bright red regions like veins
through some mineral. Several minutes passed before i
occurred to me that these markings must be canals. I was taken
completely by surprise as I had not thought of seeing canals at
a distance of 75 million miles. Their colour also was disconcert-
ing. Experienced observers such as Schiaparelli, Lowell, and
W. H. Pickering, apparently never saw colour in the canals, but
described them as dark or grey. These lines appeared distinctly
blue, the same colour as the maria.[1] In fact, they appeared to
be narrow extensions of the maria into the deserts. Pettit has
recorded the colour of the canals as olive-green and very evident
in the summer of 1939."

" Our most interesting photographs," reports Richardson,[2]
" are probably those taken in orange light on August 10, when
Mars was 39,800,000 miles away. Images of equal quality were
secured earlier, but they were too small to show much detail.

[1] The dark areas, once believed to be seas.

[2] Read as part of the Symposium on Mars at the meeting of the American Astronomical Society in New York, December 26-29, 1956.

At opposition the surface features were rendered hazy by a dust storm on Mars which apparently began about August 30. The best images of Mars, 6 and 8 mm. in diameter, taken in orange light on August 10, shows the canals *Gehon, Hiddekel, Cantabras, Agathadaemon, Ganges, Nectar, Nilokeras, Draco* and *Jamuna*. They show on the negatives as light wispy streaks. From a study of these photographs and my admittedly casual observations made hurriedly between exposures, I am convinced of the existence of streaks on Mars at approximately the position of well-known canals. They convey to me the impression of being some natural surface feature."

Before we leave Mars, its two tiny moons, Phobos and Deimos must be mentioned. Phobos, the inner satellite, revolves around the planet at a distance of only about 3,700 miles,[1] completing a full circuit of the planet in 7 hours 39 minutes. Deimos lies at a distance of 12,500 [1] miles and travels round the planet once every 30 hours 30 minutes. The remarkable thing about these satellites is their size. Phobos has a diameter of about ten miles and Deimos only about five miles. It has been suggested that they were not evolved with the planet but are captured bodies, possibly from the same source as the asteroids.

However the satellites were formed, they will certainly be of immense value when the time comes for explorers to visit Mars, for they will be used as natural " space stations."

Venus lies on the opposite rim of the " zone of habitation " as defined by limits of temperature and although the planet comes closer to us than any other body in the solar system, with the exception of the moon, some asteroids and comets and, of course, meteors, it modestly hides beneath a veil of " white cloud " which perpetually prevents us from learning anything about the surface. But although we lack the intimate knowledge we would so like to possess about the earth's " twin sister," we do know that it is slightly smaller than our own planet and that its surface gravity is a little less than it is here; in fact, a man

1 As measured from the Martian surface.

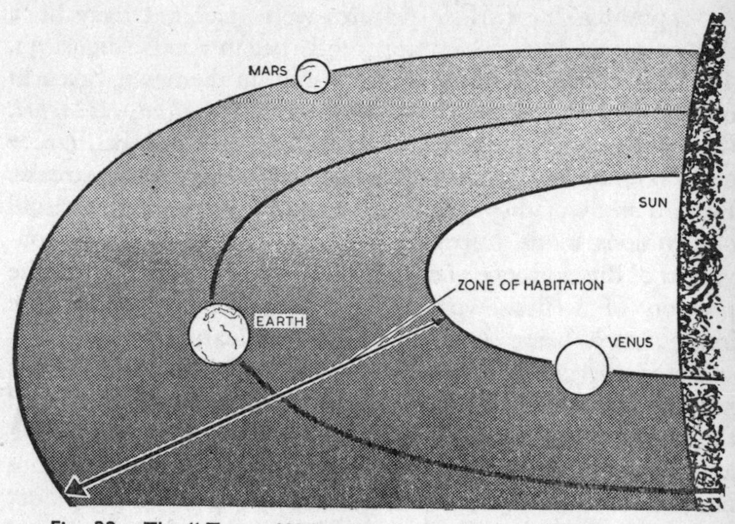

Fig. 22. The " Zone of Habitation " wherein life might be possible according to our experience (as defined by limits of temperature, ranging from the boiling to the freezing points of water).

weighing fourteen stone on earth would tip Venusian scales at about twelve and a half.

Because Venus is only 67,000,000 miles from the sun as opposed to the earth's 93,000,000, it receives about twice the amount of light and heat. Between 1923 and 1928 Pettit and Nicholson determined the temperatures as being −33 degrees C. and −42 degrees C. for the dark and bright sides respectively, referring to the top of the high cloud cover of Venus. Actually there is not a great difference between these and W. Sinton's recent results; his measurements for the uppermost layers are in the region of −39 degrees C. and are much the same for the sunlit and dark sides. The older high temperature measurements of Flagstaff and others—some reaching 43 degrees C.—have now been rejected. But since there is no fixed datum upon which to sight, no accurate assessment of the planet's period of rotation has been possible. Radio measurements made by Kraus give the rotation period as twenty-two hours seventeen minutes; Kuiper's photographic studies suggest a " few weeks." In fact we simply do not know.

The spectroscope tells us that the atmosphere is largely com-

23. *Human poliomyelites virus, magnified 85,000 times (right).*

Fig. 24. Tobacco mosaic virus, magnified 100,000 times (left).

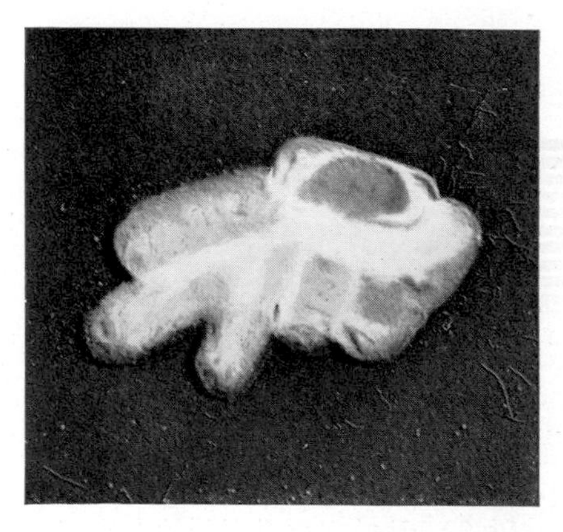

25. *Bacterium of E. colic (right).*

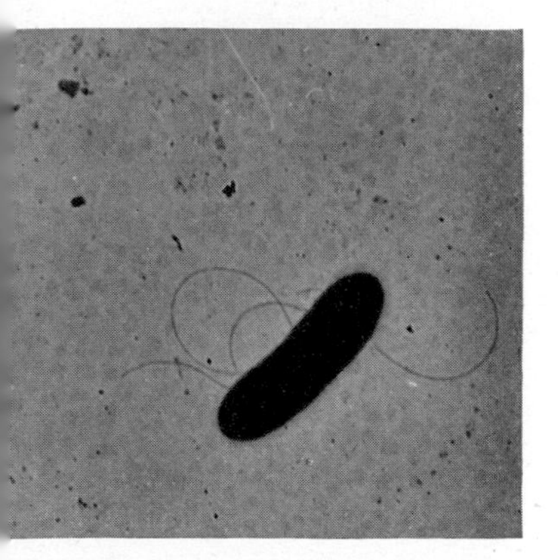

Fig. 26. Thermophilic sulphate-reducing bacterium (left).

Viruses and bacteria seen with the electronic-microscope.

rographs (1), (2) and (3), Professor R. C. Williams, Virus Laboratory, University of California. Micrograph (4), John Postgate, Chemical Research Laboratory, Teddington, (Department of Scientific and Industrial Research).

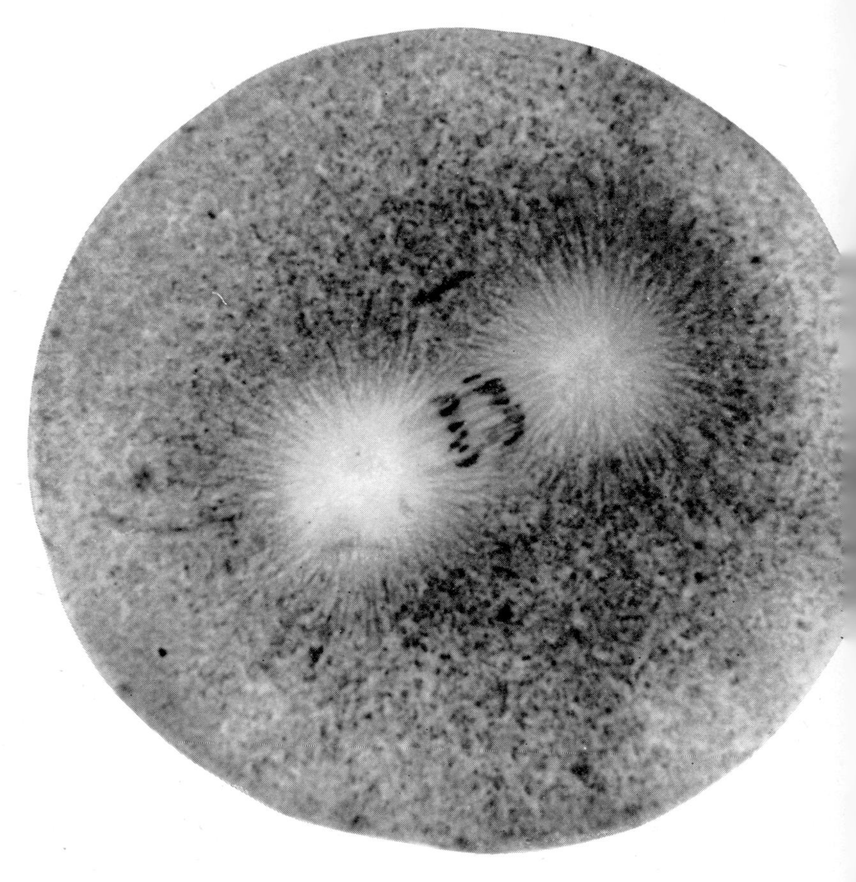

Fig. 27. The living cell. This remarkable micrograph shows a cell in the act of division, m- fied 1,300 times; the two sets of chromosomes having just separated are moving to either e the spindle.

Micrograph by Mr. R. A. Fox, Department of Zoology, University of Edinb

(Subject is actually a section of a sea urchin egg, stained with iron mæmotoxylin to reveal internal deta

posed of carbon dioxide and that it can detect no water vapour, so that whatever is the composition of the obscuring layer, it is certainly not made up of the water droplets that form earth's clouds. We must not forget though, that it has only been possible to investigate the top of the obscuring layer; conditions lower down might be quite different.

The high proportion of carbon dioxide in Venus' atmosphere strongly suggests a " greenhouse " effect and a high surface temperature which, according to some authorities, might be " around the boiling point of water." This implies a vigorous atmospheric circulation, cyclonic winds and if we are correctly interpreting the radio signals we have recently received from the planet, violent electrical storms.

On this scanty evidence, it has been suggested that Venus may be in the throes of extensive vulcanism and that the " thick " atmosphere is the result of volcanic dust being suspended in a perpetually warm fog. Wind-blown surface dusts and carbon dioxide crystals are other suggestions. At the other extreme the American astronomers F. L. Whipple and D. H. Menzel suggested quite recently that the planet may be entirely covered by sea—an ocean, in fact, of *soda water*.

Thus, Venus remains an enigma and allows us no clues to speculate on the possibility of life having evolved there, although Svante Arrhenius, the Swedish Nobel Prize winner, suggested in 1918 that it was probably in an earlier stage of evolution than the earth and might be covered in steaming jungles populated perhaps, by primeval monsters. " The humidity," he said, " is probably six times the average of that on earth or three times that of the Congo where the average temperature is 79 degrees F. We must conclude, therefore, that everything on Venus is dripping wet. The vegetative processes are greatly accelerated by the high temperature. Therefore, the lifetime of organisms is probably short."

Few people today would entertain such quaint notions on the available evidence. But it would be foolish, on the other hand, to be too dogmatic and state categorically that life could not possibly exist under such " adverse conditions," for as we saw in the previous chapter, recent research has shown that forms of life based on different biochemistries might flourish elsewhere in conditions which would spell death to the animal and vegetable worlds that surround us. One has only to remember the sulphur bacteria, and the bacillia Boracicola which can exist happily in a saturated solution of boric acid, to quote just two examples. Such organisms as may exist on other planets may be a long way from Arrhenius' " monsters " but, if life, however lowly, can once gain a foothold, who can say what new forms evolution may ultimately bring?

Now that the microscope has brought such startling evidence of " alien " life-forms within the range of our own experience it might be prudent for biologists generally to discard the medieval attitude that the earth is the measure of the universe, as their compatriots in astronomy did many years ago.

CHAPTER FOUR *The Expanding Universe*

" . . . if there is an underlying oneness of all things, it does not matter where we begin, whether with stars, or laws of supply and demand, or frogs, or Napoleon Bonaparte. One measures a circle beginning anywhere."

CHARLES FORT.

DOES LIFE exist elsewhere in the universe? If, by this question, we mean " intelligent life " (whatever that may mean), confirmation is unlikely to be found in space travel unless, in some far distant age we are able to venture into the depths of interstellar space in search of planetary systems which may be associated with other suns. So great are these distances that to enable human beings to leave our own solar system and travel to even the nearest stars, whole generations would have to live and die to give their descendants the chance of reaching the destination system. This gives some idea of the scale of distance in the universe for it would take a space ship travelling at a speed of a million miles an hour almost 3,000 years to reach the nearest star. There is, on the other hand, the possibility of the earth itself being visited by some alien intelligence.

Thus, although we shall probably discover a great deal more about the origin of life when the planets of our own system are explored, the question of " intelligent life " is likely to remain.

Therefore, we are compelled to consider the problem from the standpoint of reason. " Does life exist elsewhere in the universe? " The answer must surely be an unqualified " yes! ", for if there is no life elsewhere which pretends to consciousness, man can be nothing but a freak, fashioned by the blind forces of chemical reaction and his lofty ideals, philosophies and religions nothing but echoes of a singularly negative existence.

If, however, we accept the view that life is abundant in the universe, present ideas that life was created by a series of highly fortuitous events are no longer tenable and the biologist must seek a more subtle explanation for man's presence.

Biological science is at pains to emphasize the precarious conditions under which life first began on the earth. We learn of the chance creation of the protein molecule—and of the sequence of events that led up to this supreme moment: how certain chemical elements had to be present in the atmosphere, how the atmosphere had to be modified by sunlight, and how the elements of the earth first had to be worn down to prepare a "soup of organic compounds," such as acetic acid, methyl alcohol, and formaldehyde, in the ancient seas. Throughout the story as told by the biologist, the operative word is CHANCE. So much depended on the earth being the right distance from the sun, the sun having the right temperature, and the earth possessing the right chemical composition at the right time.

Bernal has suggested that the first protein molecule was so complicated that it must have needed some template upon which it could be assembled. He has suggested that the surface of clayed mud might serve this purpose. Short-wave radiation from the sun would be needed to provide energy for building up the molecule. Haldane [1] has largely supported the theory that "life originated as the result of a very 'improbable' event, which, however, was almost certain to happen given sufficient time and sufficient matter of suitable composition in a suitable state."

The mathematical probability of life occurring under the conditions suggested here is, of course, at tremendous odds—yet still possible! One recalls the monkeys Jeans set to strum haphazardly on a typewriter; given time, he said, one of them would produce a Shakespearian sonnet.

There is nothing at all to suggest that life was not the result of an improbable event; but if it was, then it is very unsatisfactory from the point of view of man. His universe is without purpose, and he has no greater meaning than the most lowly by-product of the physical world.

What is the alternative? It is that life is as much a characteristic of the universe as matter and energy and that life will

[1] "The Origins of Life," *New Biology,* No. 16, Penguin Books, London, 1954.

emerge under diverse chemical conditions. That is to say, if life had not evolved in the way it did upon the earth, it would have found an alternative route and expressed itself in some other way. In this hypothesis, life—like planetary systems—may be far from an isolated or accidental happening in nature.

The very pertinent fact remains that planets may be very common throughout the universe, and out of the hundreds of millions of stars which populate each of the millions of galaxies, there must be many which have planets of the right chemistry, dimensions and distance from the parent star to support life. Why, indeed, should biological development be limited to one isolated speck in the universe?

Even now we are discovering that living things cannot be divorced from the inanimate. Many fields of scientific inquiry, astronomy, geophysics, biochemistry and microbiology, are combining to give us an exciting glimpse into the vast potentialities which exist in the universe—or at least, that special fragment of it that we occupy. With each new discovery, it is becoming more and more evident that evolution is a continuous process stretching unbroken from the primordial hydrogen atom to man himself. And it begins to look as though life is as much a characteristic of the universe as the stars themselves.

At the same time, one must proceed with caution; it would be wrong to suggest that science has reached definite conclusions on this matter. In fact, until we can determine with certainty how the sun's family of planets came into being, it is, to say the least, a trifle premature to interpolate from this and assert categorically that planets are common throughout the universe. On the other hand, even if the solar system was the result of some freak cosmic upheaval, the material content of the universe is so vast that, on the basis of chance alone, similar freak conditions *must* have arisen. At present, a simple statistical analysis is our only yardstick.

There is, nevertheless, growing evidence that life is not restricted to the earth alone. The seasonal change in colour observed on Mars strongly suggests the presence of vegetation. If life, however lowly, exists on our neighbour planet, can life and the processes which bring it into being be quite as restrictive as science has previously supposed? It is still possible that Mars, in common with the earth, may have arisen by some rare cosmic accident but even so, the evolution of life from inorganic materials will have taken its separate course on both worlds.

However, in the final analysis, we shall still not be certain about these issues until more is known about the planets and how they were formed. Astronomy and astrophysics can help provide some of the answers but it will not be until man can explore the planets at first hand that it will be possible to make real progress. Herein lies one of the most important reasons for space flight—the prospect of turning observational astronomy into experimental astronomy, with all its exciting implications for our greater understanding of the universe.

The study of astronomy is as old as man himself. At a conference on Science and World Order in 1941, Dr. Joseph Needham said: "Whenever modern man climbs to the top of a newly conquered mountain of intellectual achievement, he finds that the Greeks had shot an arrow there 2,000 years before. But acquaintance with Chinese culture shows that if he looks again, he is apt to find a Chinese arrow there too."

The Greeks and Chinese relied on a highly developed knowledge of mathematics and philosophy in their investigations, not on instruments such as our scientists have at their command, so that the answers they obtained are quite remarkable to us even today. Democritus of Abdera, who lived in the early part of the fifth century, for example, had a remarkably modern turn of mind. He projected his ideas well beyond the moon to embrace the whole of surrounding space, which he believed to be filled by thousands of stars too small to be seen individually but whose light united to give us the ribbon of light characteristic of the Milky Way.

He also visualized the moon as a world of deep valleys and high mountains, and even declared that there was an infinite number of worlds of differing sizes with many suns and moons separated by unequal distances.

Digging deeper into Democritan theories, we find that this remarkable Greek recognized the evolutionary stages through which worlds were going. Some, he asserted, were coming into being, many had reached full growth and others still were declining into eventual disintegration. And he declared that life could not exist on some because of the conditions which prevailed on them.

Eratosthenes of Cyrene calculated the circumference of the earth and measured its inclination to the ecliptic. But we cannot be sure whether his measurement was accurate or not because we do not know which of the two values, given to the *stadion* unit of measurement, he used. One of these gives us the figure of 24,662 miles; the actual circumference is 24,902 miles.

Names like Timocharis, Aristillus, Hipparchus, Heraclides, Aristarchus and Poseidonis ring through the Mediterranean history of the time, but little evidence of their work remains. This was probably due to the rising Christian Church's determination to establish the uniqueness of its religion by stamping out countless literary treasures they fanatically assumed to be remnants of other cults, and the Arab view that nought compared with the wisdom of the Koran.

Paradoxically, the Arab school of astronomy flourished during the first fifteen centuries of the Christian world wherein the study of the stars was virtually a lost art.

It is one of the ironies of history that for nearly sixteen centuries through war and other stupidities this knowledge was lost. Not until the times of Copernicus, Galileo and Newton did science begin to rediscover the ancient truths and disclose the humbling nature of our relationship with the universe.

According to ecclesiastical scholars of the time, man lived in a geocentric cosmos, where the earth was God's flat, four-cornered footstool with the sun, moon, planets and stars all on strings in an immovable, eternal crystal sphere.

For most of his short history man has been firmly convinced that his planet was scarcely older than himself, and more often than not he has resisted clues that every now and then came to light. In 450 B.C. Herodotus discovered fossil remains of shellfish deep in the Lybian desert, and deduced that the Mediterranean must have encroached far inland at one time. Two thousand years later Leonardo da Vinci found similar remains in Italy and came to the same conclusion.

But Christian man has always had many conflicting ideas about his world and how it began. At first its origin was regarded as the outcome of a divine act and, by studying the religious texts, there were people who even attempted to discover when this remarkable event had occurred. For example, in 1654, after a detailed study of the Old Testament, Archbishop Ussher of Armagh announced that creation had taken place in the year 4004 B.C. This date was actually printed in authorized versions of the Bible and thereafter, for a century or more, it was heresy to suggest an earlier origin. Nevertheless, Ussher's estimate did not entirely convince one Bishop Lightfoot, who felt it lacked precision. His studies led him to the conclusion that it had certainly happened in 4004 B.C.—*on October 23, at 9 o'clock in the morning*!

Man's conceit was supreme—until Copernicus showed that the earth was in fact *moving round the sun*. This, however, was a dangerous philosophy and did not obtain wide circulation until after Copernicus's death in 1543. And so the sun and not the earth became the hub of the universe. Yet religious ideas still held a strong influence over scientific thought. Giordano Bruno was actually burnt at the stake for teaching that the sun was not the centre of the universe but only one of many stars.

These old ideas persisted right up to the nineteenth century when, in turn, the sun's importance in the scheme of things was diminished by the knowledge that the stars that filled the heavens were, in fact, other suns—many much larger than our own; they extended away from the earth in all directions as far as existing telescopes could penetrate. Even then it was thought that the sun and the planets were near the centre of the stellar system and that all the stars in the universe were contained within a relatively small volume, perhaps a few hundred light years in extent. It was only in 1923 that the 100-inch telescope on Mount Wilson gave the proof that this incredible collection of stars was in fact a giant island universe—a rotating disc of gas and stars so vast that light takes 100,000 years to cross from one side to the other. More astonishing still, the many diffuse objects which were previously believed to be part of this local system were clearly seen to be outside it. They were, in fact, other vast island universes similar to our own (Fig. 8). It is estimated today that no less than 6,000 million of these lie within the range of our largest telescopes.

No longer could the earth be regarded as the supreme citadel of the worlds. From being " the centre of all creation," the sun's family of planets was relegated to a minute speck among probably more than 30,000 million suns on an island universe—itself but a fragment in a boundless ocean.

In the face of all that had been learned, could man still believe that he was the " specially created " ? To believe that of all the vast stellar systems the earth was the sole abode of life now seemed entirely ludicrous. How, then, did man enter the picture? To attempt any answer to this question, we must return our thoughts to basic principles.

It is believed that pure hydrogen is the " raw material " from which all things are created. It was from atoms or ions of hydrogen gradually united by the process of evolution—taking the pathway of galaxies, stars and planets—that the more complex elements were formed with which we are familiar on the earth, and which in turn led to the whole cavalcade of life.

But where did the primordial hydrogen come from? To offer any useful hypothesis, it will be necessary to construct a model of the universe on the basis of our latest knowledge and speculations. In the universe we are conscious of immense forces at work in giant stellar systems which permeate all space. We believe that the universe is expanding—that all the island galaxies are receding from each other at great speed. And because this universe has mass and hence, gravitation, we have the hypothesis that " space is curved." A ray of light emitted from the earth would theoretically return to its point of origin, bent inward by the accumulative effect of gravitation acting upon it. Straight lines, it appears, can no more exist in the universe than they can on the surface of a sphere.

This universe, which Einstein defined as " finite but unbounded," cannot be visualized any more than one can visualize an electron, but both can be expressed mathematically. By this means it has been possible to arrive at an estimate for the size of the universe. Dr. Edwin Hubble of Mount Wilson Observatory studied selected areas of the heavens in order to determine the average density of matter that exists in the universe. His conclusion, after years of patient research, was that there is ·000000000000000000000000000001 gramme of matter per cubic centimetre of space; from this a value for the curvature of space was obtained, from which the radius of the universe was found to be 210,000,000,000,000,000,000 miles, or 35 *billion light years.*

And yet, as we have seen, the universe is not static; it is expanding rather as a soap-bubble can be made to expand. The universe represented in this model is not the interior of the soap-bubble but the film out of which the bubble is blown.

The clue that the universe is expanding is obtained from spectroscopic studies. A spectroscope is an instrument which splits light into its characteristic colours or wave-lengths—red, orange, yellow, green, blue, indigo and violet. All self-luminous bodies emit light which is characteristic of the chemical elements they contain and under spectrum analysis, these show up as graduations of colour and can be compared with the spectral lines of familiar elements found on earth. In this way, it has been discovered that the sun contains hydrogen, helium, carbon, calcium, and a whole range of other chemical elements.

Not only does the spectroscope enable us to establish the chemical composition of distant stars and galaxies, but it can also tell us whether a star or galaxy is moving away from us or towards us and at what speed. This is the so-called "Doppler effect," which is best explained in terms of sound waves. If an express train dashes through a station emitting a whistle, a person waiting on the platform will notice that the whistle remains at high pitch all the while the train is approaching and then, as the train rushes past, the pitch suddenly drops. The effect is due to the train's motion in relation to the observer. The sound waves shorten as the train approaches and lengthen as the train recedes.

In a similar manner, light waves emanating from a distant

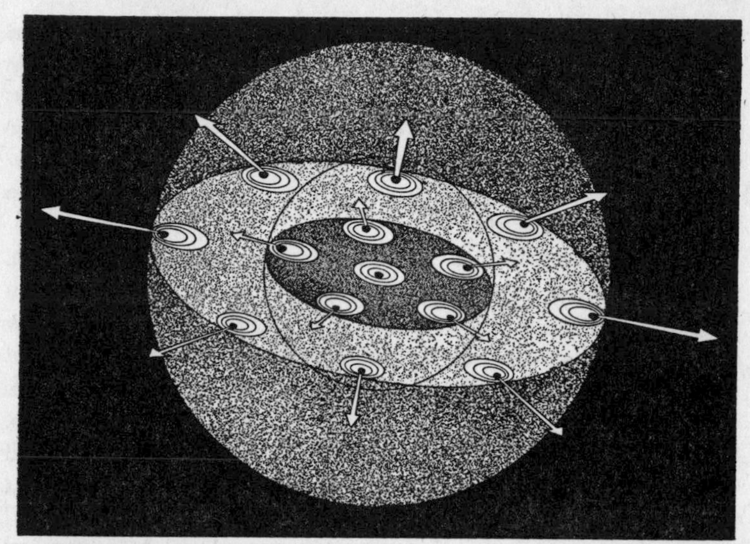

Fig. 28. Flight of the galaxies. As recently as 1914, man's comprehension of the universe did not extend beyond the confines of the local galaxy (centre). Today, with the aid of giant optical telescopes, astronomers can probe 2,000 million light years into space and have discovered thousands of millions of galaxies, all apparently receding from each other at a speed which is proportional to their distance. In surveying this vast assembly, we must be careful to avoid the idea that we are " fixed observers " at the centre of the universe. Nothing in the universe is at rest. Consequently, when we say that a galaxy at the limit of vision is moving away from us at one-third the speed of light, we must remember that any observers in that distant galaxy will be thinking precisely the same about our own system. To them, our galaxy will be a faint receding image, in fact, wherever we may be in space, we should have the impression that all the surrounding galaxies were moving away from us and that their rate of expansion was proportional to the distance. The inner circle in the diagram represents the limit of observation with the 100-inch telescope on Mt. Wilson ; the outer circle, that of the 200-inch telescope on Mt. Palomar.

galaxy are lengthened as a result of the galaxy's relative motion away from the earth; the whole spectrum is moved slightly towards the red and by measuring the displacement, it is possible to determine the velocity at which the galaxy is receding.

The " red-shift," as the effect is called, indicates that the universe is expanding—that the galaxies everywhere are moving steadily apart. The greater the distance from ourselves, the " fixed observers," the faster is the speed of recession; it turns out that if you double the distance, you double the speed at which these bodies are receding. The nearest galaxies appear to be rushing away from us at speeds of several million miles an hour, while the farthest ones appear to be moving outwards at over 200,000,000 miles an hour. Galaxies lying beyond the vision of our present telescopes would presumably have greater speeds; and those at twice the range of the 200-inch telescope would be moving away from us at approximately the speed of light. How does this agree with the premise that no material body can travel faster than light?

To answer this we must exchange our "soap-bubble universe" for a balloon and cover the surface of the balloon with inelastic spots to represent the island galaxies. If we blow up the balloon to represent the expansion of the universe, it will be observed that it is actually the space between the galaxies that stretches. Mark a particular spot and expand the balloon. Regardless of the spot you have chosen, all the other spots will move away from it. While the spots themselves have remained essentially the same size, the space between them has stretched out proportionately so that, if you stop the expansion and re-examine the balloon, the nearest spots to the one you have marked will have moved a small distance away and the more remote ones a proportionately greater distance. Therefore, as Hoyle puts it: "The distances between the galaxies increase not so much because they move in the sense we are used to in everyday life, but because the space between them gets stretched." The reddening of light occurs because the time taken for that light to reach us increases owing to the stretching of space.

Nevertheless, from the point of view of an observer on the earth, the galaxies which exist at more than twice the range of the 200-inch telescope will be moving away from us with a speed greater than that of light, so that the light they radiate cannot break through to us against the expansion that is taking place. In view of this, it seems that we shall never be able to see galaxies at distances greater than 4,000,000,000 light years. This is the extent of the observable universe.

Why does the universe expand? It was the late Sir Arthur Eddington's view that approximately 91 thousand million years ago, all the matter in the universe was collected together in the form of a "homogeneous nebula," the volume of which was far smaller than the space we can now explore with telescopes. He suggested that irregularities within the nebula caused the gases to condense into localized clouds with space in between them; being no longer joined together, the local condensations began to recede from one another, making their own space as they went. Each of these condensations became the galaxies which we now observe.

Others have suggested that the universe began with a great primordial explosion in which all the matter arising from it was sent forever outwards from its point of origin. Canon Lemaître, of Lourain, replaced Eddington's primordial nebula with a single primordial atom which gave birth to the substance of the universe in one incredible explosive instant.

This idea has by no means been abandoned. In the United States, Gamow, Herman and Alpher have modified and extended the original theory. They envisage a universe beginning 5,000 million years ago with a concentrated source of neutrons and radiant energy. The neutrons would be dispersed by radiation which at the same time, they suggest, would provide the fantastically high temperatures to enable the neutrons to be built up into the familiar elements. This would fill the universe with a gaseous background of atoms of every kind, in exactly the proportion in which they have been discovered from the abundance of hydrogen to the comparative rarity of the heavy elements such as uranium. According to the theory, after 250 million years, the radiation would no longer drive the gaseous material apart but would tend to concentrate it to form galaxies and stars.

Against this theory, recent investigations by Spitzer, Schwarzschild and Wildt have shown that the heavier elements in the stars are widely variable, with " young " stars possessing from twenty to one hundred times more of these elements than the " old " stars. It is extremely difficult to reconcile this situation with the idea of a universe having an " explosive " beginning.

All these theories postulate a fixed point in time for creation and imply a fixed duration for its existence. Hydrogen, by far the most abundant material in the universe, is continually combining into more complex elements within the stars. But when all the hydrogen is used up, we can expect all the stars in all the galaxies that do not become nova to evolve towards black dwarfs.[1] We should end up with a dead universe.

Others have suggested that the universe might be expanding and contracting in turn, and still others that the atomic processes at work in the stars (whose energy is derived from the conversion of hydrogen into helium) send out energy into space in the form of radiation which recombines into the background material to create new galaxies, and so on, in a continuous cycle. There is no evidence at all for the former theory; the second, to say the least, is highly conjectural.

The theory of an expanding universe introduces one great difficulty. It is, as Hoyle observes, the fact that at the observed rate of expansion, it would take only about 10,000,000,000 years—about a fifth of the lifetime of the sun—to empty the sky of all the galaxies we can now observe.

It is this " thinning out of the universe " that has led Bondi, Gold, Hoyle and others, to a revolutionary theory, which suggests that matter is in the process of being *continually created* throughout the universe.

The new material does not appear in a concentrated form in small localized regions but is spread throughout the whole of space. According to a calculation by Hoyle, the average rate of appearance amounts to no more than one atom in the course of a year in a volume equal to St. Paul's Cathedral. Although this may seem a very small rate when judged by ordinary standards, it is not small when one remembers that it is happening everywhere in space. The total rate for the observable universe alone would be a hundred million, million, million, million, million tons per second. It is from this " background material," says Hoyle, that new galaxies are continually being evolved to maintain a uniform density in the expanding universe.

Where does the material come from? Material simply appears—it is created. At one time the various atoms comprising the material do not exist and at a later time they do. In this way, Hoyle's universe, though constantly changing through

[1] A star which has completed its stellar life. Presumably there are many dead stars which may be so termed. They are not directly observable, and the only hope we have of finding them is when they occur in a binary system, and thus reveal their presence by their perturbing influence on companion bodies which can be seen.

expansion, retains a similar structure throughout as new galaxies condense out of the background material to fill the space left by the mutual recession of the galaxies.

The " continuous creation " theory is, of course, very far from being universally accepted and attempts are now being made to discover exactly how closely it matches up with observational results. If creation *is* taking place uniformly in every part of the universe, we should expect to find galaxies in certain preselected volumes of space differing widely in age. Unfortunately, the methods by which the ages of remote galaxies can be determined is still uncertain—and it is precisely those galaxies which are near the limit of observation that are the most useful for this purpose.

A valuable tool in furthering this intriguing quest is the radio telescope whose development stems from the discovery of an American engineer, J. C. Jansky, who found in 1931 that radio waves were reaching the earth from outer space.

What was this mysterious radiation and whence did it come? The first serious attempt to confirm Jansky's discovery prior to the Second World War was made by Grote Reber of Illinois, an amateur radio enthusiast who constructed the first radio telescope in his garden.

Thirty feet in diameter, Reber's instrument was designed to receive on a wave-length of about two metres and could be aimed at any part of the heavens. It revealed that the signals were strongest near the centre of the local galaxy and along the plane of the Milky Way where the greatest concentration of stars is to be found. Yet, when the instrument was aimed at individual bright stars, the response was completely negative. At first, what appeared to have been discovered was a new type of astronomical body, dark or faintly luminous, but capable of transmitting a powerful radio signal. It was a type, moreover, that appeared to be distributed as uniformly throughout the galaxy as visible stars.

For a short while, this idea of a " radio-star " persisted, but then the theory was advanced that the radio signals originated in the highly rarified hydrogen gas of interstellar space. Remarkably enough, the germ of this theory came from a young Dutch research student by the name of Van der Hulst during one of the last clandestine meetings the astronomers of Leiden Observatory were able to hold during the German occupation.

The essence of the theory is that, to emit radiation, the outer electrons of an atom have to rearrange themselves as they do, for example, to emit light-waves. Van der Hulst pointed out that the hydrogen atom's single electron could spin in two different ways with respect to the magnetic field associated with the nucleus and calculated that if the electron changed from one spin to another the atom would transmit a signal on a wave of twenty-two centimetres. Theoretical considerations suggested that the switch in spin would occur no more than once every 11,000,000 years per electron. However, although the density of hydrogen atoms in interstellar space is extremely low—about one in every cubic centimetre—the gas clouds are so vast, especially near the centre of the galaxy, that a continuous emission would be set up which could be detected by the right kind of equipment.

The tremendous boost radio and radar was given during the war provided the new science of radio-astronomy with plenty of stimulus to develop when, at length, the equipment could be put to scientific use. The first important post-war discovery came in 1948 when Bolton and Stanley in Sydney, Australia, and Ryle and Smith in Cambridge, announced almost simultaneously that radio waves were coming from localized sources in space. One source was discovered in the constellation of Cygnus and the other in Cassiopeia; neither coincided with a known star. Then, in the spring of 1951, America, Australia and Holland announced that they had succeeded in detecting a weak signal from a hydrogen cloud in the Milky Way. Grote Reber's original findings were confirmed. There was no connection between visual astronomical objects and the strange radio emissions from space.

In the continued search for further " radio " sources, it was discovered that radio waves were coming from the Crab Nebula (Fig. 48), the gaseous debris of a supernova first seen by Chinese astronomers in 1054. Then, another source was discovered where Tycho Brahe had seen a supernova in 1572, although no discernible evidence remains. The remnants of no fewer than

Fig. 29. *The 200-inch telescope on Mount Palomar, astronomy's largest optical instrument. With its aid, astronomers can probe 2,000 million light years into space.*

Mt. Wilson and Palomar Observatories.

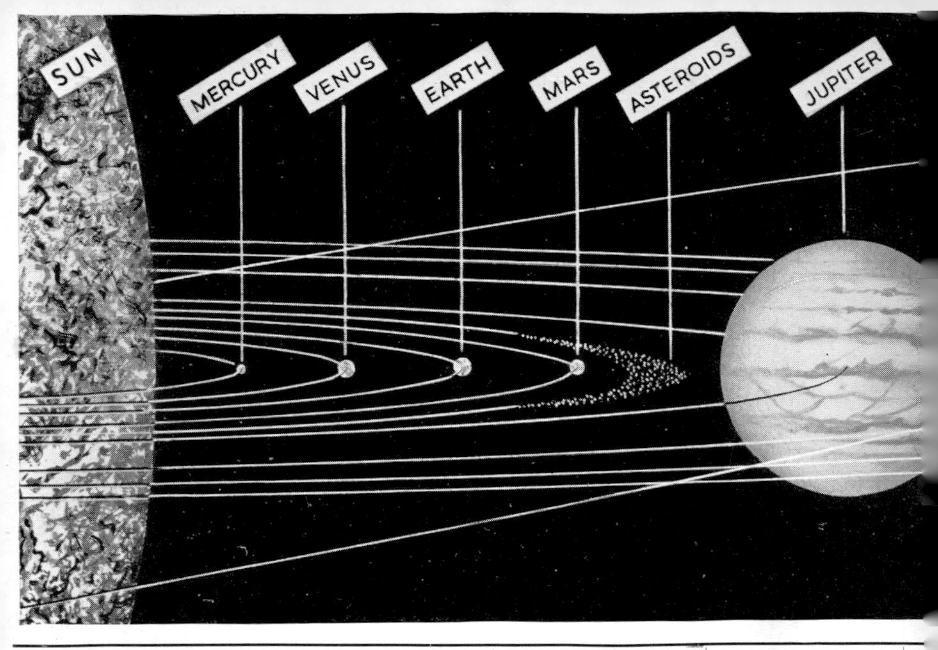

Planet	Diameter (miles)	Distance from Sun (millions of miles)			Period of Revolution (year)	Mean Orbital Velocity (m.p.h.)	Period of Rotation			Mass (in terms of Earth's mass)	Temperature	E Ve (
		Min.	Mean	Max.			Day	Hrs.	Min.			
MERCURY	3,000	28·6	36·0	43·4	0·241	108,000	88	0	0	0·0370	700° F. (sunlit face), —423° F. to —405° F. (dark side)	
VENUS	7,600	66·8	67·3	67·7	0·615	78,120	30	0	0	0·8260	—38° F. at top of clouds (W. Sinton). Varies little between dark and sunlit face	
EARTH	7,927 (Eq'l.) 7,900 (Polar)	91·45	93·0	94·56	1·000	66,600	—	23	56	1·000	See page 50	
MARS	4,200	126·2	141·7	157·2	1·881	54,000	—	24	37	0·10860	80° F. (noon, tropical belt) —95° F. (night)	
ASTEROIDS	480 miles dia. (Ceres) largest, 300 (Pallas), 240 (Vesta) and 200 (Juno) —ranging to dust particles											
JUPITER	88,700 (Eq'l.) 82,800 (Polar)	460·5	483·9	507·3	11·862	29,160	—	9	50	318·4	—305° F. (at top of atmosphere)	3
SATURN	75,100 (Eq'l.) 67,200 (Polar)	837·8	887·2	935·6	29·458	21,600	—	10	14	95·2		2
URANUS	30,900	1,700·0	1,784·0	1,868·2	84·015	15,120	—	10	45	14·6		1
NEPTUNE	33,000	2,768·8	2,797·0	2,825·2	164·788	12,240	—	15	48	17·3		1
PLUTO	3,600	2,758·0	3,670·0	4,582·0	247·697	10,440		?	?	0·1	—380° F.	

Fig. 30. Chart of the solar system, showing the Sun and planets to scale with tabulated c
porting the theory that the planets conde

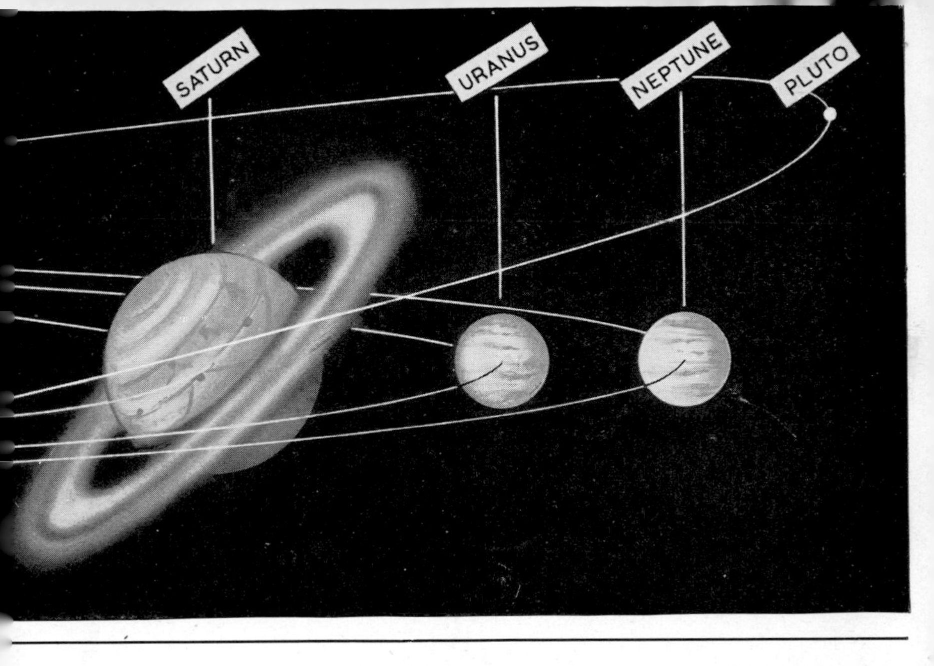

Physical Characteristics

ıely rarified atmosphere of heavy gases possible, though high temperature and low gravitational attraction means y more appreciable atmosphere will have evaporated into space. Planet perpetually turns one face towards the sun. rature extremes so great that, on sunward side, lead would melt and on dark side, nitrogen would liquefy. Surface ons, rocky and barren. No satellites.

clouds (largely carbon dioxide) perpetually shroud surface. Surface conditions unknown. No satelli tes.

phere of 78% (by volume) nitrogen ; 21% oxygen; 1% argon, with a trace of carbon dioxide and other gases. rominent features : polar caps and vast fluid oceans covering ¾ of planet's surface. Vegetable and animal life. ant species : *homo sapiens* (degree of intelligence). One satellite ; Moon, 2,160 miles dia., mean distance from planet, 0 miles ; minute trace of atmosphere—density perhaps 1/10,000th that of Earth's believed to be present.

phere of carbon dioxide (possibly more than 95%) with some argon and trace of carbon dioxide and other gases. rominent features : ochre-coloured " deserts " covering ⅝ of planet's surface, dark areas which undergo a seasonal in colour (suggestive of vegetation) and polar caps which rapidly diminish in the Martian summer. Two satellites ; s 10 to 14 miles dia., Deimos 5 to 7 miles dia. ; mean distance from planet 5,828 miles and 15,000 miles respectively. y captured asteroids. Gravitation of Deimos so low that a man could achieve escape-velocity merely by jumping off.

of tiny planetoids (probably more than 100,000 of irregular rock formation). May be debris of a planet destroyed by r's powerful gravitation, or residue of an unformed planet when solar system was born.

enormous pressure of atmosphere, surface may be thick layer of solid hydrogen. Jeffreys and Wildt suggest planet onsist of a rocky core approx. 44,000 miles in diameter surrounded by a thick layer of ice overlaid by a dense phere thousands of miles deep, principally of methane and ammonia. Planet's fast axial rotation causes violent atmos- storms, detectable on Earth as radio signals. Most prominent and mystifying feature, " red spot " discovered in 1878, ng an area approximately 24,000 miles long and 7,000 miles wide. May be caused by violent expansion of hydrogen er atmosphere. Twelve satellites ; largest Io 2,300 miles dia., Europa 2,000 miles dia., Ganymede and Callisto 3,200 dia. and others with diameters ranging from 20 to 100 miles, between 112,500 and 15,000,000 miles from planet. four revolve counter-wise to planet's rotation. Four largest discovered by Galileo in 1610.

atmosphere composed of methane and ammonia. Great three-ring system girdling planet at a distance of approxi- y 130,000 miles, believed composed of dust and rock particles all travelling in same plane and orbit. May be debris of tes smashed by planet's powerful gravitation. Nine satellites ; largest Mimas 370 miles dia., Titan 3,500 miles dia. hoebe 200 miles dia., ranging between 117,000 to 8,054,000 miles from planet. Possibly other satellites exist. Titan noon in Solar System with an (appreciable) atmosphere, largely methane.

mely low temperature—ammonia freezes and atmosphere consists largely of methane. Planet's axis tilted at more ight angles to the sun, so that its five satellites, revolving in the plane of the equator, pursue orbits which are almost al to planet's orbit. Five satellites ; largest Ariel 600 miles dia., Umbriel 400 miles dia., Titania 1,000 miles dia., on 900 miles dia., ranging from 120,000 to 365,000 miles from planet.

ane atmosphere ? Two satellites ; Triton 3,000 miles dia. and Neroid 200 miles dia., at 221,500 miles and 5,000,000 respectively from planet. Triton, revolves counter-wise to planets rotation.

considerably out-of-plane with other planets. May have originated as a satellite of Neptune (see text). So cold that phere has probably solidified. No satellites.

s in most cases are nearly circular and lie approximately in the same plane, strongly sup- a whorl of gas with the Sun at its centre.

Fig. 31. The Moon, region of the giant crater Clavius 146 miles across, obtained with Palomar's 200-inch telescope.

Mt. Wilson and Palomar Observatories

3,000 of these " exploding stars " are now believed to have been pin-pointed by this technique.

Without the radio-telescope, it would have been impossible to fully explore the Milky Way for the actual centre of the galaxy is hidden from us by obscuring matter—gas and dust—which optical instruments are powerless to penetrate. However, by studying the radio emissions from various parts of the heavens, radio-astronomers have been able to confirm that our galaxy is made up of at least five spiral arms emerging from a central " hub " and that our solar system occupies an unprivileged position in one of the trailing arms.

A further step in probing the riddle of the radio emissions was taken in 1950 when a large radio-telescope began to explore the *extra-galactic* nebulæ. The galaxy in Andromeda was found to emit radio waves like those of our own galaxy—and far into the depths of space other galaxies responded in exactly the same way.

Some of the radiations we receive come from galaxies so far away that the radiation they emit takes 2,000 million years to reach us.[1] Others are known to originate from galaxies which are actually in collision. Martin Ryle of Cambridge has suggested that the thousands of unidentified radio sources may, in fact, be colliding galaxies which are so far distant that they are beyond the limit of penetration of the largest telescopes. If this is true, we are studying the condition of the universe as it existed perhaps 2,000 million to 3,000 million years ago—not long after the world we know came into existence.

So far we have not been able to produce an experimental check on how the universe began, since optical telescopes can take us back only about 2,000 million years. However, with the advent of new radio-telescopes, such as the giant instrument at Jodrell Bank, Cheshire, we may be getting near to a test of Gamow's classic theory that the universe originated from a primordial explosion. With the greater sensitivity afforded by this immense aerial system, we shall be listening to events even further in the past—events which may hold vital clues to the perplexing riddle of creation.

[1] Light waves and radio waves, of course, both travel at the same speed, approximately 186,000 miles per second.

It is a fundamental to the theory of continuous creation that the universe expands at a constant rate. Therefore, evidence that the universe once expanded at a faster rate than it does today—admissible in the case of an " explosive " origin—would strike a mortal blow at the alternative theory.

Professor Ryle has tentatively suggested that if encounters between the more remote galaxies are, on the average, more frequent than they are among nearer galaxies, this would argue against continuous creation.

If, on the other hand, creation started " explosively " from some concentrated source, the universe should have been denser in the past than it is today. Since radio signals from the more remote galaxies take billions of years to reach us, collisions between the galaxies we are now detecting must have occurred —according to this theory—when the universe was younger and more concentrated. Therefore, if encounters between galaxies are more frequent in distant space than they are nearer home, this would argue against the steady-state universe of continuous creation.

Other important results have come from the United States, where Allan A. Sandage of Mt. Wilson and Palomar Observatories has been studying the speeds of six clusters of galaxies about a billion light years distant. If the universe is expanding at a uniform rate, as suggested by continuous creation, the clusters should be receding at a speed which is in direct proportion to their distance. In fact, calculation appears to show that the clusters are moving away from us about 6,200 miles per second *faster* than predicted, implying that the universe was expanding more rapidly a billion years ago.

These, it must be emphasized, are only tentative results for, handicapped as we are by instruments still chained to the earth, we cannot be certain whether our measurements and interpretations are correct. Do the enormous distances that these radiations travel from distant galaxies affect the results? Is the expansion of the universe alone accountable for the " red shift," on which so many of our measurements are based? We may have a very long time to wait before science can be certain one way or the other.

But continuous creation is a tidy theory. It disposes of the idea that the universe is " running down " and it explains how, despite its observed expansion, the universe maintains its density.

Moreover, because it replaces the old theory of a universe moving towards decay with a " live " universe of infinite possibility, it makes a strong appeal to the human spirit. *It is a story with a middle—the now—yet without beginning or end.*

CHAPTER FIVE *Out of the Cosmic Void*

> *"The stream of knowledge is heading towards a non-material reality; the universe begins to look more like a great thought than like a great machine."*
>
> SIR JAMES JEANS
> "The Mysterious Universe."

MATTER COMPRISES everything around us. It is the firm ground beneath our feet, the air we breath, the great fluid oceans, the trees and all forms of life. It can be solid like rock, strong like iron—and complex like man. And it can be converted into the most violent form of energy.

But what exactly *is* matter? A Greek philosopher, by name Anaxagoras, gave thought to this problem in the year 500 B.C. What would happen if he took a bit of matter—a gold nugget, perhaps—and halved it, then halved the halves, then halved the halves of the halves, then halved the . . . Where would he end up? To Anaxagoras it seemed he could go on forever without reaching the point at which he could halve no more.

In relating this little episode, Dr. J. G. Feinberg [1] admits that had he considered the composition of matter at that period, he too would no doubt have arrived at the same conclusion. "I should certainly not have gone conjuring up hypothetical final bits of matter and called them atoms," he says. How, indeed, could Anaxagoras have conceived that matter could be made up of finite, discrete, building blocks, at which point further halving must cease?

And yet, in the fifth century B.C., there was Democritus expressing his faith that the universe could not be fashioned from a formless sort of matter with no fundamental character. It needed an indestructible germ of matter: the *a-tomos* particle, or atom.

Democritus' atom had to be indestructible. Otherwise, there would be no stability in material things and it was their very

1 "The Atom Story," Allan Wingate, Ltd.

stability that preserved their individuality. So he postulated an atom which could neither be smashed from without nor disrupted from within. "This eternal, invulnerable atom, reasoned Democritus, was the medium through which matter in living form perpetuated itself in its own particular image. The very birds, with their distinctive, gaily coloured plumage, wrote his Roman disciple Lucretius, could not reproduce young in their own complex images unless they could pass along germs of matter so indestructible and unchangeable that they reappeared—unaltered 'spring after spring'." Here, says Dr. Feinberg, Lucretius or Democritus strayed somewhat from atomics into the field of genetics. This they were not to know, as the science of genetics was not to be born until about twenty-five centuries later! And yet their arguments held good because, in common with all matter, the genes which determine our heredity are structures formed from and dependent on the "ultimate" and "indestructible" atom. We have many centuries to traverse before we come to the division of the "ultimate" and the destruction of the "indestructible"; and even today the atom is still basically the inviolable fixture of matter on our earth. Those chemical reactions which are the very foundation of life are dependent on the "indestructibility" and "constancy" of the atom for the precision with which they repeat themselves from individual to individual, from generation to generation.

So the desk at which we write is not as "solid" as it appears. And if you take any material substance, as Anaxagoras did, and keep dividing it, you will eventually arrive at the smallest portion that can exist in a free state and still manifest all the properties of the substance—this we call a molecule. Split a molecule of water and you no longer have water, but two atoms of hydrogen and one of oxygen: this is the point where we leave the world of chemical compounds for a world where "material" things no longer exist; where matter is replaced by "energy in little packets" called atoms.

Present ideas on the structure of the atom visualize it as a miniature solar system, with a central nucleus (sun) surrounded by orbital electrons (planets). In every case but one, the atomic nucleus is made up of an integral number of protons and

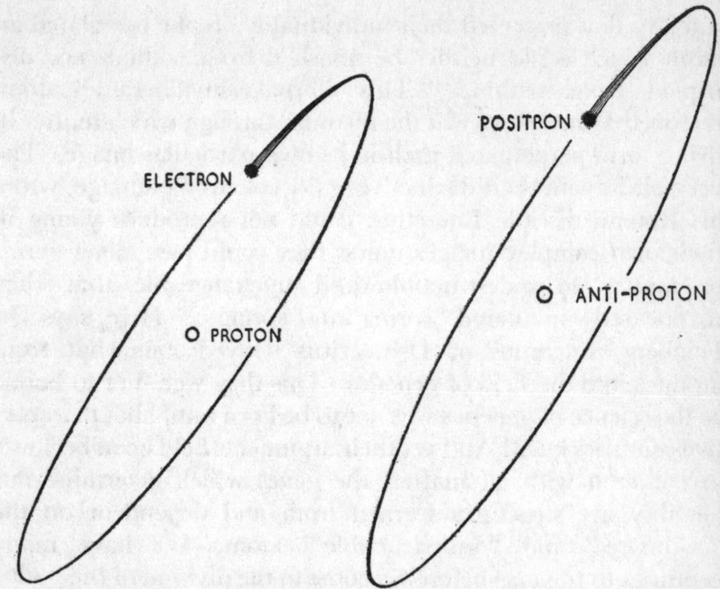

Fig. 32. The hydrogen atom—" building block " of the universe.

Fig. 33. An atom of anti-hydrogen.

neutrons. The exception is the hydrogen atom which has only one proton in its nucleus, and one orbital electron. The proton is the fundamental positively-charged particle of matter, whereas the neutron, as its name implies, is neutral in character, having no electrical charge. Despite the fact that protons are 1,837 times as massive as electrons the positive electrical charge on the proton is equal to the negative charge on the orbital electrons.

Atomic nuclei then are built up of an integral number of " particles." The simplest and lightest atom, hydrogen, possesses one proton and helium two protons, whilst at the other end of the atomic table, we have uranium (the heaviest natural element) with ninety-two protons. It is found that the number of negatively charged orbital electrons exactly equals the number of positively charged protons in the nucleus; therefore, the electrical charge on the atom itself is zero.

By far the greatest part of an atom is empty space. If you imagine the nucleus as a golf ball, the outermost electrons would circle the nucleus at a distance of about one-third of a mile. If it were possible to eliminate the space in all the atoms that make up a human being, so that all the particles of the nuclei and the orbital electrons were packed together, nothing would remain of bones, tissue and a proud brain, but a minute trace. So if we think of " solid matter " as consisting of a vast collection of suns (atomic nuclei) and planets (circling electrons) bound together in one immense system, like galaxies, we shall have as good a picture as we are likely to obtain.

This conception of matter as being composed largely of empty space explains why atomic particles can pass through apparently solid materials with the ease with which light passes through glass. If we were ignorant of the structure of the atom, we should expect the particle to bounce back like a ball rebounding from a wall. In fact, Rutherford showed that the average alpha particle can shoot right through any substance without encountering an atomic nucleus capable of deflecting it—so much space exists within the structure of matter (Fig. 37).

We have seen that hydrogen has one proton in its nucleus and one orbital electron; helium has two protons (and two neutrons), with two orbital electrons, while the sodium atom has twenty-three protons and twelve electrons. How, then, do atoms build up into chemical compounds?

Let us take just two simple examples. Sodium atoms and chlorine atoms do not have one ring of orbital electrons; they have three. The sodium atom has two electrons in the inner ring, eight in the second ring, and one in the third. The chlorine atom has seventeen orbital electrons, two electrons in the inner ring, eight in the second ring and seven in the third. The fact that these atoms have an odd number of electrons in the outer ring makes them unstable and they readily combine. In the case of sodium and chlorine, the seven outer electrons of the chlorine atom seek to capture the lone outer electron of the sodium atom. The sodium atom, by giving up its outer electron, becomes stable and positively charged, while the chlorine atom becomes negatively charged. The result is that the two atoms are rendered mutually stable, forming a molecule of sodium chloride (common table salt).

Similarly, an atom of oxygen is unstable in having two electrons in the inner ring and six outer electrons; eight electrons

Fig. 34. An atom of the metal sodium (11 electrons, 2 in the first ring, 8 in the second ring, and 1 in the third).

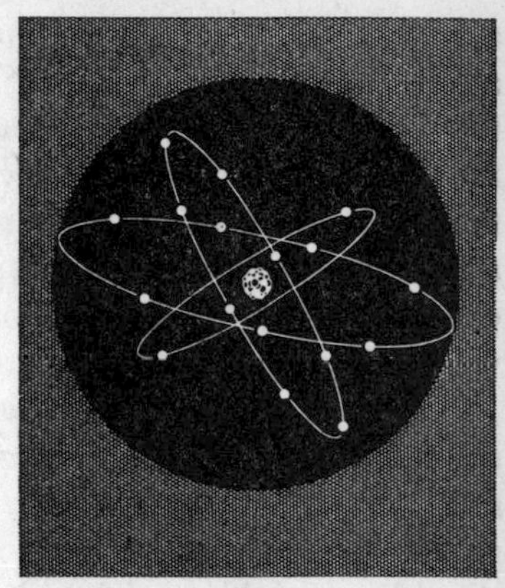

Fig. 35. An atom of the gas chlorine (17 electrons, 2 in the first ring, 8 in the second ring, and 7 in the third).

are required in the second ring to achieve stability. Hydrogen, on the other hand, possesses only one orbital electron so that it is impossible for individual atoms of oxygen and hydrogen to combine. But where two hydrogen atoms and one oxygen atom are present, the oxygen atom will capture the electron from each hydrogen atom and combine to produce a molecule of water (H_2O).

Separate atoms will not combine if both have surplus electrons or require additional electrons to complete the outer ring. However, with over eighty " sociable " types of atoms an infinite number of atom-combinations are possible; these may be as simple as water or as complex as the albumen in the white of an egg, which is made up of thousands of atoms of oxygen, hydrogen, nitrogen and carbon and is very complex in structure. Here we have an illustration of the way in which nature is continually experimenting, the restless, ever adventurous atoms sometimes combining, sometimes rejecting—yet ever creative. It is this characteristic of atoms to combine that has enabled the " lifeless " base elements, hydrogen, nitrogen, oxygen, carbon and others, to produce life in all its variety and profusion—from the lowly plant virus to the complexity of man. " In this respect," writes Dr. Feinberg, " life and language are in much the same boat. In our alphabet there are only twenty-six letters. If those

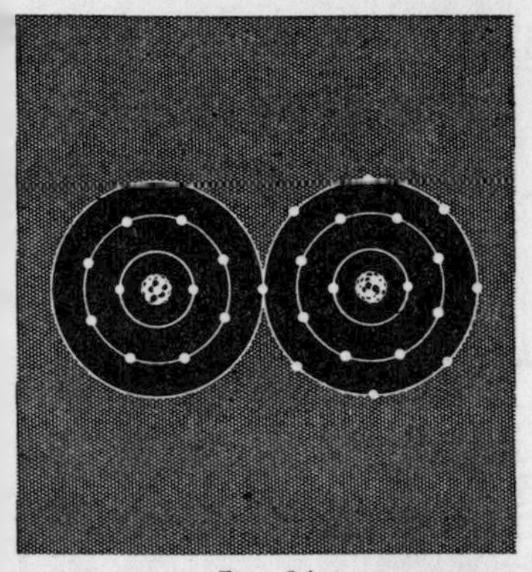

Fig. 36

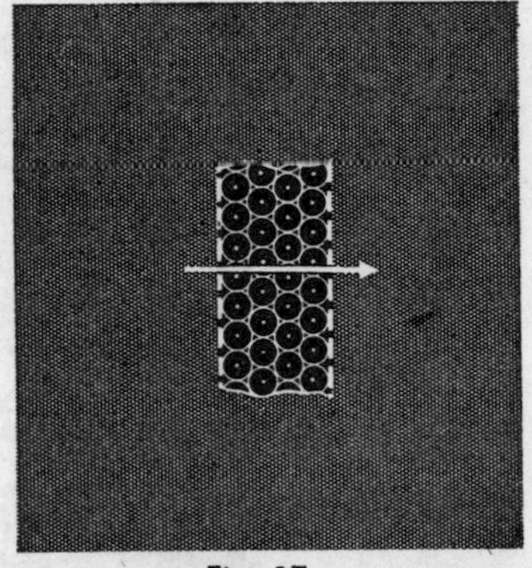

Fig. 37.

Fig. 36. Sodium and chlorine atoms combine to form a molecule of sodium chloride—common table salt.

Fig. 37. Diagram representing a section through a piece of tin-foil, showing the atomic structure. In practice, millions of atoms would constitute the thickness of the foil. (A small particle of dust would contain something like a thousand million million atoms.) Yet so much space exists in the atomic structure of matter that atomic particles will shoot right through the foil without encountering an atomic nucleus.

letters were never combined with each other our vocabulary would be severely limited; aaaaa, . . . bbbbb, . . . ccccc, . . . and so on. But permit them to mix and mingle and you get that wonderful collection of letter-combinations—*words* we call them—which has given us the glorious and living literature of Chaucer, Shakespeare, Dickens, and their fellow writers. Yes, even letters, which by themselves are dull and lifeless, spring to life when they combine!"

And it is the same with the atoms of the earth.

Modern research into the microcosm stems from the development of particle accelerators. The first one was built by Cockcroft and Walton in 1932. It cost only a few hundred pounds to build and was installed in one of the rooms of the Cavendish Laboratory in Cambridge; it produced about 800,000 volts. Today the efforts to generate particles of higher and higher energy have led to the construction of "atom smashers" capable of producing particles which are 3,000 time more energetic.

The cyclotron, which owes its origin to Professor E. O.

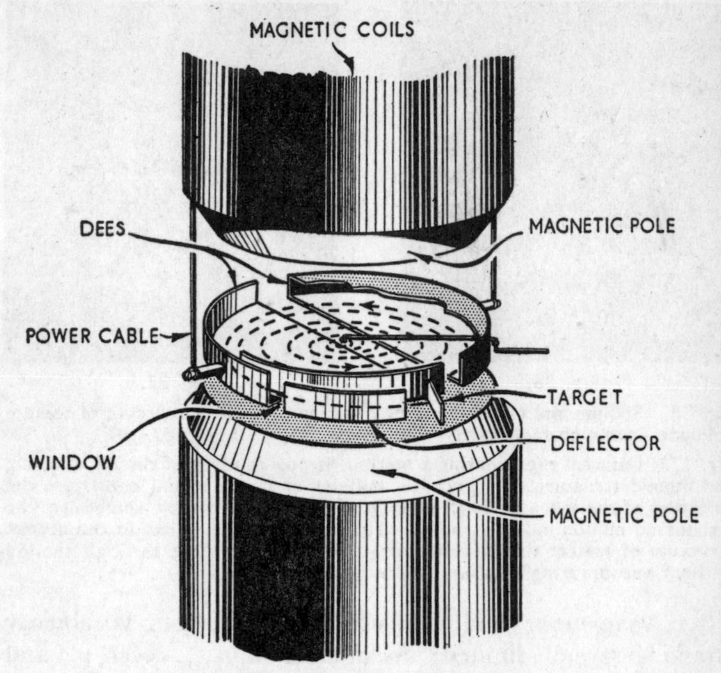

Fig. 38. Principle of the Cyclotron.

Lawrence of the University of California, works on the principle that a steady magnetic field will exert on an electrified particle a force acting at right angles to its course. Under such conditions, a particle being accelerated by electric forces will, as its speed increases, pursue a spiral course, taking the same time to complete one circuit whether the radius is large or small.

The cyclotron itself consists of two hollow metal chambers, called D's because of their shape, placed a small distance apart inside a larger chamber from which air can be exhausted. The dee chambers are, in fact, semi-circular electrodes, fed from separate power cables. Situated above and below this sealed " working compartment " of the atom-smasher are the poles of a powerful electro-magnet (Fig. 38).

The idea of the device is that particles originating in the centre of the accelerator, enter one of the dees and travel in a small circle under the influence of the magnetic field. Thereafter, at each stage, when the particles reach the gap between the D-shaped electrodes, the polarity of the dees is reversed. In this way, the particles are continually accelerated, travelling round and round on increasingly wider paths until they reach the circumference of the dees where they can be directed at a "target plate." (Bombardment of the "target" releases sub-atomic particles from the material of the plate, sometimes creating new particles.)

Particle accelerators are essential equipment in any atomic research centre and, in fact, the cyclotron has led to a whole family of similar machines with which, by refinements of technique, even higher velocities have been achieved. In the case of the synchrotron, for example, the particles are introduced at as high an energy as possible, and powerful magnetic fields are so arranged that the particles, while being accelerated by electric fields, are constrained to as near a circular path as possible. In this way, electrons and other sub-atomic particles have been driven up to velocities within a small fraction of the speed of light.

In a later chapter, we shall see that as the speed of light is approached, the mass of the accelerated particles increases quite sensationally,[1] so that the faster they are made to travel in the accelerator, the "heavier" they become. This has the effect of throwing the whole machine out of balance, tending to make the particles' arrival at the gap between the dees mis-time with the reversal of polarity and actually sets a limit to the cyclotron's operation.

To a large extent this difficulty is overcome in the synchro-cyclotron and other accelerators, in which the frequencies of the accelerating voltages are variable, so that the two factors can be matched, or "synchronized," up to extremely high velocities. In the synchro-cyclotron, particles receive about twenty million accelerating impulses per second; neutrons would make 10,000 revolutions in one-thousandth of a second and reach velocities of 80,000 miles per second. The Berkeley Bevatron, at the Radiation Laboratory, University of California, has actually

[1] The mass of an electron moving at about 150,000 miles per second is more than half as much again as it is at rest; electrons moving with 99·98 per cent of the speed of light are 1,000 times more massive.

accelerated electrons to a velocity of 186,000 miles per second, *which is virtually light-speed.*

With these high-powered accelerators, physicists hope to increase our knowledge of the atomic structure and the mysterious forces that bind the nucleus, and ultimately, to improve our understanding of the interpenetrating fields of energy that are the essence of material creation.

A further increase in our knowledge is expected when new giant accelerators are put into operation within the next few years—in particular, the Alternating Gradient Synchrotron, now under construction at Brookhaven National Laboratory, Long Island, New York.

Previous atom-smashers have been strong enough to smash target atoms and also produce the sub-atomic particles known as mesons, which are believed to be the cosmic " cement " that binds the nucleus. Experiments with these machines, however, have disrupted earlier ideas about the mechanics of atoms. More and more different sub-atomic particles have been found; a recent count listed twenty-six, which suggests that our present concept of the nucleus as being merely composed of protons and neutrons may have to be seriously revised. Many kinds of mesons are known, as well as other particles whose existence and physical properties are still enigmatic.

To help straighten out this dilemma, physicists are hoping that yet more powerful atom-smashers will reveal the number of sub-atomic particles, show how they are held together, and disclose their properties. The significance of the new Brookhaven accelerator is that the 25,000 million electron volts it will produce is fairly close to the energies inherent in stable natural atoms. Thus, for the first time, scientists will have a device that can still the swift-moving mechanics of the atom and permit a more thorough study of it.

The Alternating Gradient Synchrotron, or A.G.S., at Brookhaven National Laboratory, will take the form of a giant steel and copper hoop 842 ft. in diameter, housed in a circular underground tunnel half a mile long (Fig. 57). Full power will be attained by accelerating a beam of protons at energies of 25,000 million to 30,000 million electron volts. This is four times the energy of the proton beam from the Bevatron, one of the two [1] most powerful accelerators now in operation, and ten times the energy produced by the Cosmotron, which it will overshadow at Brookhaven.

The protons will be started on their journey to these colossal energies by means of a 100 ft. long, 50 million electron volt linear accelerator, which in itself will be one of the largest of its type anywhere in the world. The particles will then be accelerated around the half-mile long vacuum chamber and kept in their circular orbit by means of 240 strong focusing magnets. Acceleration will be accomplished by means of twelve radio frequency accelerating stations. Within one second, the protons will travel about 370,000 times around the machine and reach their top energy of about 25,000 million electron volts.

This remarkable machine, which is expected to be in operation by 1960, has been made possible by the discovery in 1952 by a team of American scientists of a new method of magnetic focusing. This makes it possible to keep the beam of atomic particles on its course without deviating more than one five-hundredths of an inch over 100 ft. Were it not for this strong magnetic focusing, the beam would get off course long before it reached its target at the end of its 175,000 mile journey. The giant ring of magnets will be buried in a subterranean cement tunnel, 17 ft. 8 in. high and 18 ft. wide; this will be covered with 5 ft. of earth.

Part of the tunnel will include a building containing the target. This building will be heavily shielded with concrete and it is hoped that physicists will be able to work in it for short periods. There will be another building from which the A.G.S. can be operated by remote control.

The giant machine will give a burst of 1,000 million accelerated particles every three seconds; later this may be stepped up to a hundred times as many particles a pulse.

Total cost of the atom-smasher, with its administration building and a power house with a 30,000 kilowatt generator, will be about 26 million dollars.

Will there ever be bigger atom-smashers than this? The European atomic organization, CERN, is building one with the

[1] The other, a new 8,300 million-volt atom-smasher, is at the Dubna Nuclear Research Institute, near Moscow.

same potential energy as the A.G.S. And at a meeting of the American Physical Society in 1956 a design was reported for a machine capable of accelerating nuclear particles to energies of 1,000,000,000,000 electron volts.

In the summer of 1956, a remarkable experiment by Dr. E. Muller, Professor of Physics of the Pennsylvania State University, revealed for the first time the existence of atoms as separate entities.

The methods used to obtain this result are almost as remarkable as the result itself. First, the tip of a tungsten wire, so fine as to be invisible to the eye, was sharpened to a point.[1] This incredibly fine " needle " was placed inside a glass tube with a fluorescent screen at one end and the tube inserted into a special " field ion " microscope. The temperature of the microscope was then reduced to −420 degrees F. by introducing liquid hydrogen. Helium gas provided the ions and the tungsten tip produced a highly magnified picture on the fluorescent screen. Photographed by a special camera, the result was a clear view of pearl-like atomic clusters magnified 2,750,000 times (Fig. 61).

So far we have been dealing with atoms of ordinary matter. However, in October 1955, a particle was discovered which opened up a new vista of atomic structures. This particle—the *anti-proton*—does not exist in the nuclei of ordinary atoms which, as we have seen, are composed only of protons and neutrons (Fig. 55).

Although its existence was predicted twenty-five years ago, anti-protons were not discovered earlier because they occur only at high energy, such as is now available with the Berkeley Bevatron, which is capable of shooting protons with an energy of 6,200 million electron volts.

To produce the new particle, a powerful beam of protons was aimed at a copper target plate inside the Bevatron chamber (Fig. 39). When a proton of this power hits a neutron in one of the copper atoms, a new proton and an *anti-proton* are created. In the process, about 2,000 million electron volts of energy are

[1] The needle was sharpened by chemical etching and smoothed down to atomic steps by annealing.

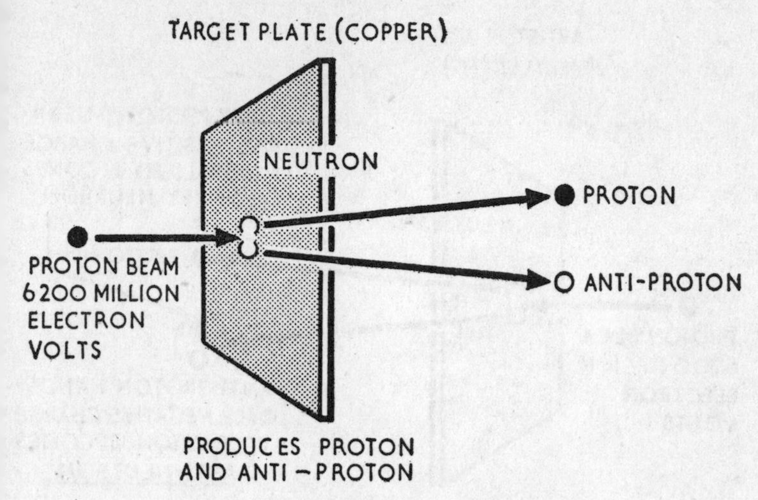

Fig. 39. Creation of the anti-proton.

transformed into matter. This, of course, is precisely the reverse of what happens in the atomic bomb, where matter is turned into energy.

In ordinary circumstances, the life of the anti-proton is short for as soon as it encounters a normal proton it is annihilated, both particles being transformed into energy. However, the anti-proton *is* stable in a vacuum and does not disintegrate spontaneously, which lends support to the idea of creating *anti-matter*.

Anti-hydrogen would be the simplest type of anti-atom. Instead of being an ordinary hydrogen atom with a central proton and a planetary electron (Fig. 32), an atom of anti-hydrogen would have as its nucleus an anti-proton with an orbiting positron (positive electron) (Fig. 33).

Positrons were first discovered in 1932 as a result of research into cosmic rays. These high-energy particles, whose origin is still one of the primary mysteries of physics, bombard the earth as an invisible rain from outer space; they are nature's own "atom smashers." When cosmic rays encounter atoms in the earth's atmosphere, other particles are produced, among them positrons. Like the anti-proton, the lifetime of a positron is measured in micro-seconds, for as soon as one encounters a normal electron, both particles vanish in a burst of energy.

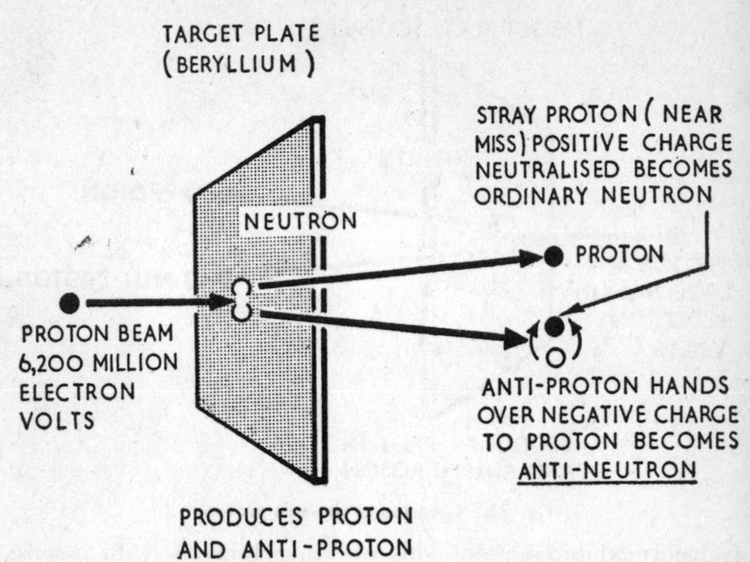

Fig. 40. Creation of the anti-neutron.

Now that both anti-protons and positive electrons have been produced, anti-hydrogen is a theoretical possibility; but the creation of larger atoms of anti-matter would require *anti-neutrons*. When in September 1956, it was announced that subsequent experiments with the Bevatron had, in fact, yielded anti-neutrons (Fig. 40), all the constituents of " anti-matter " had been created.

To produce the anti-neutron, the 6,200 million electron volt protons were aimed at a beryllium target; among the shower of atomic particles released, those with a negative charge (largely mesons and a few anti-protons) were separated by the Bevatron's strong magnetic field. Most of the anti-protons were annihilated (transformed into energy) upon encountering an ordinary proton, but when an anti-proton *passed close* to a normal proton without actually hitting it, it merely *transferred its negative charge*. The proton became an ordinary neutron and the anti-proton, having lost its negative charge, became *an anti-neutron with a reversed magnetic field.*

When an anti-neutron encounters a normal neutron, the result once again, is mutual annihilation.

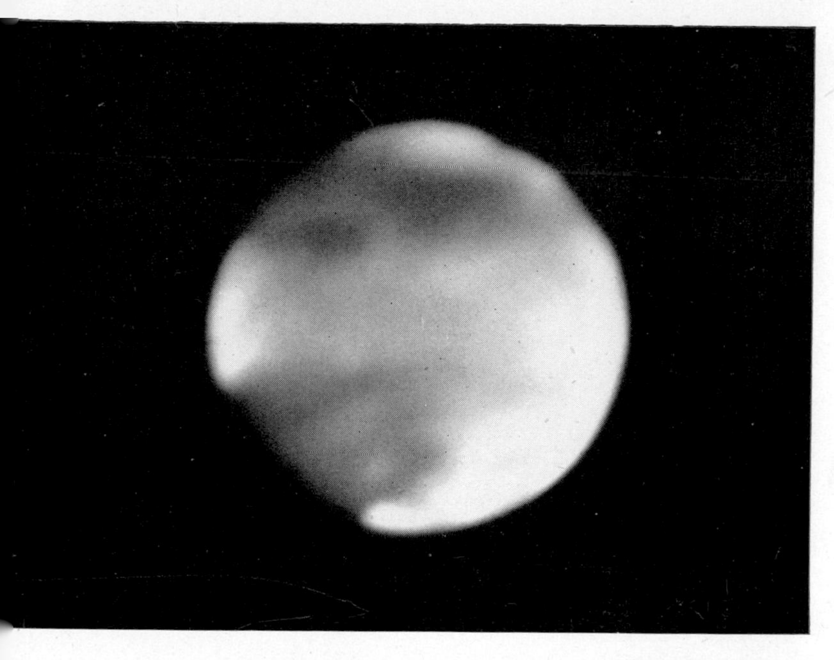

Fig. 41. Mars, photographed in blue light, reveals the extent of the atmosphere.

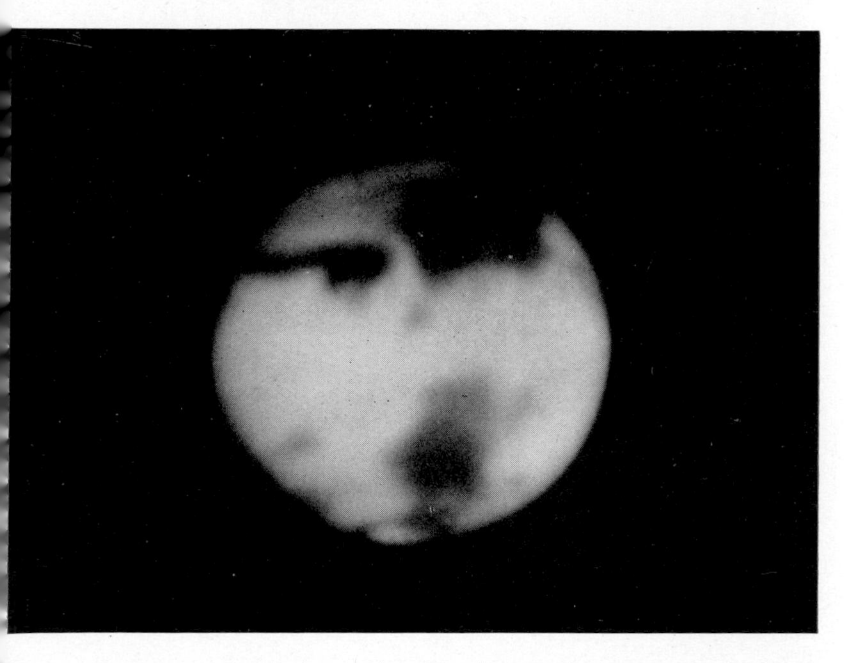

Fig. 42. The famous dark areas (or maria), suspected regions of vegetation, are clearly seen in this photograph of Mars taken in red light.

Mt. Wilson and Palomar Observatories.

Fig. 43. Jupiter—the satellite Ganymede can be seen in the top right hand corner. The lo oval marking is the famous Red Spot.

Fig. 44. Saturn: An early theory of the planet's fabulous ring system was that it was formed fr a moon that came too close to the planet and was broken into fragments by the strength of gravitational field. More recently, it has been suggested that the rings may be composed of crystals.

The giant planets, Jupiter and Saturn, photographed with the 200-inch telescope.

Mt. Wilson and Palomar Observato

The ability of scientists to create these particles leads us to inquire whether anti-atoms, and hence *anti-matter*, could occur naturally in the universe. It appears quite impossible for the two to exist within our own galaxy for, in contact with each other, the result would be catastrophic. But we cannot be quite so certain about other galaxies existing in splendid isolation in space which, theoretically, could be constructed wholly of anti-matter.

No observational checks that could be made from the earth would determine whether a particular galaxy were made of ordinary or anti-matter for the light that carries the images of these objects, being electro-magnetic in character, is entirely neutral and would have exactly the same appearance whatever its source. Thus, direct observation or spectrum-analysis would yield no clue.

There appears to be only one way in which confirmation might be obtained. Earlier, we have seen that, in their huge wanderings, galaxies within the same group sometimes collide. Normally, this has no greater consequence than friction between the interstellar gas and dust, for the distance between the individual stars is so great that it would be rare for stars actually to collide. However, if such an encounter took place between *unlike* galaxies, wholesale annihilation would take place among the gas and dust particles. Even so, this would not be the complete disaster; the space separating the individual stars would effectively " insulate " the star fields, with the result that the two galaxies would merely be stripped of their interstellar matter. This, in itself, would release enormous energies and a significant increase in brightness.

A number of galaxies have been photographed in the act of collision and, in fact, one such example (in the constellation Cygnus) does suggest that much more energy is being released in the form of radiation than is apparently normal in this kind of encounter.

At the same time, it is extremely difficult to reconcile the idea of ordinary matter and anti-matter existing side by side in the same universe; not that there is anything particularly novel about anti-matter, which merely represents the "reverse image" of ordinary matter and proves the symmetry of nature.

Scientists would be disturbed if it were otherwise.

The problem—if indeed a problem exists—is how galaxies of opposite kinds could have been created. If the universe began, as Gamow and others believe it did, as the result of some immense primordial explosion, then it is felt that all but one kind of matter would have been annihilated during the first micro-seconds of creation. Neither does the alternative theory of " continuous creation " offer any more hopeful solution, for if one assumes that atoms of *both* matter and anti-matter are appearing uniformly throughout the universe, how would the two kinds of matter get sorted out and condensed into separate galaxies? Probably, the answer is that only one kind of matter does exist and that some other effect is responsible for the extra brilliance associated with the colliding galaxies in Cygnus. It may be, but at the present stage of our knowledge, we cannot be sure.

But supposing a world of anti-matter did exist, what would it be like? Dr. Emilio Segre, one of the physicists who first created the anti-proton, summed up the situation as follows: " As far as physics is concerned, the anti-world would be identical with our world. An anti-egg would taste like an ordinary egg of you, too, were an anti-man."

CHAPTER SIX *The Strange Duality of Light*

"The limits of our spectrum do not inhere in the sun that shines, but in the eye that marks his shining. Beyond each end of that prismatic ribbon are ether waves of which our retina takes no cognisance . . . Even thus, I venture to affirm, beyond each end of our conscious spectrum extends a range of faculty and perception, exceeding the known range but as yet indistinctly guessed. . . . Beyond the red *end, of course, we know . . . that organic processes are constantly taking place within us, which are not subject to our control, but which make the very foundation of our physical being . . . The faculties that lie beyond the violet end of our psychological spectrum will need more delicate exhibition, and will command a less ready belief . . . yet it is* that *prolongation of our spectrum upon which our gaze will need to be most strenuously fixed. It is* there *that we shall find our enquiry opening upon a cosmic prospect, and inciting us upon an endless way."*

F. W. H. MYERS
(written before 1896).

WE GAIN our impressions of the universe through eyes which have evolved over millions of years according to the kind of radiation which is abundant in our surroundings—the light we receive from the sun, a star of average brightness. Had our evolution taken place on some other planet remote from its sun or in another part of the universe, our eyes might have been tuned to another part of the waveband. If our sun were a star of the red giant variety our eyes would be tuned to the infra-red, which, like other types of radiation that pervade interstellar space, is invisible to the eyes we actually have.

Space is filled with all kinds of radiations whose nature would have remained forever unknown but for the ingenious instruments man has devised to extend his knowledge. For example, it has been discovered that radio waves are reaching the earth from outer space. One should not conclude from this that intelligent beings in some other part of the universe are trying to communicate with us. It is simply that some of the radiation we receive from astronomical sources lies within the band of wave-lengths used in broadcasting. There is nothing particularly strange about this for although the visible light we receive from the sun and the radiations of a radio transmitter seem quite different, in fact they are physically the same, electro-magnetic radiations differing only in wave-length.

As the electro-magnetic spectrum in Fig. 52 shows, ordinary radio waves have a wave-length of a few hundred metres, short wave radio employs wave-lengths of a few metres and radar occupies the scale between a metre and a centimetre. Further down the scale, between a few hundredths and a ten thousandth of a centimetre, we find infra-red radiation. Visible light, the narrow wave-band to which our eyes are sensitive, lies within about 0·00008 to 0·00004 of a centimetre with ultra violet radiation, X-rays and gamma rays still lower down the scale.

Of the sixty octaves discovered to cover the whole of the electro-magnetic radiation frequency range, only one takes the form of visible light. So that any attempt to solve the mysteries of the universe in terms of what our eyes can see would be futile—like a man whose hearing is limited to just two notes of an octave striving to appreciate a symphony.

Unlike sound waves, which require air or some other material medium in which to propagate, light waves travel freely in the vacuum of interstellar space. To explain this, scientists of the nineteenth century assumed that space was filled with an all-pervading luminiferous medium which they called " the ether." They believed light waves were transmitted through the ether in much the same way as sound is transmitted through the air.

As it turned out, the ether was an unnecessary assumption, and it is now generally recognized that electro-magnetic waves do not need a material medium to sustain them.

What, then, are these peculiar emissions? All electro-magnetic radiations travel at the same velocity—approximately 186,000 miles per second—and according to Einstein the speed of light is absolute—it cannot be surpassed by any material body. Later on, we shall see that Einstein's famous Theory of Relatively introduces some strange ideas about travel at near optic velocities, affecting the increase of mass of a body and contraction in time. But first, we must understand something about the properties of the radiation itself.

We know that the stars are steadily converting their own substance into radiant heat and that the sun actually radiates four million tons of its substance into space every second. This means that over the past 100 million years, more than 10,000 million million million tons of the sun's mass must have been ejected [1] in the form of light and heat. The earth and the planets intercept but a minute fraction of this radiation, the bulk of which is destined to travel on endlessly through space. Similarly, the radiation from millions upon millions of other suns has been pouring into space, so that although we often speak of "empty space," space is never really empty; in the darkest recesses of the universe, there is always starlight. And, as Einstein taught us, radiant energy cannot very well be divorced from matter.

It was a firm belief in the nineteenth century that radiation was emitted in an unbroken stream of waves through the "ether." Today, we believe that radiant energy actually travels through space in discontinuous units called *quanta*. To put the situation crudely, the old theory regarded the emission of light as a jet of water issuing from a hose, while the new one pictures it more as a stream of bullets fired from a machine gun. When we sunbathe, the sensation of heat arises from the bombardment of our skin by innumerable "bullets" or quanta, of radiant heat. In a similar manner, the colour sensations we receive result from the bombardment of our optic nerves by light quanta.

How then, one may ask, does the quantum theory agree with our earlier assertion that electro-magnetic radiations, light and wireless waves, differ according to *wave-length*? If light is composed of streams of sub-atomic "bullets," how can it at the same time possess wave characteristics? The strange fact is that light has a double nature. Although radiant energy is composed of particles (photons), it also has the property of waves, as can easily be demonstrated.

When a beam of light is directed onto a metal plate a shower

[1] A quantity which, however, represents less than one-millionth of the sun's total mass.

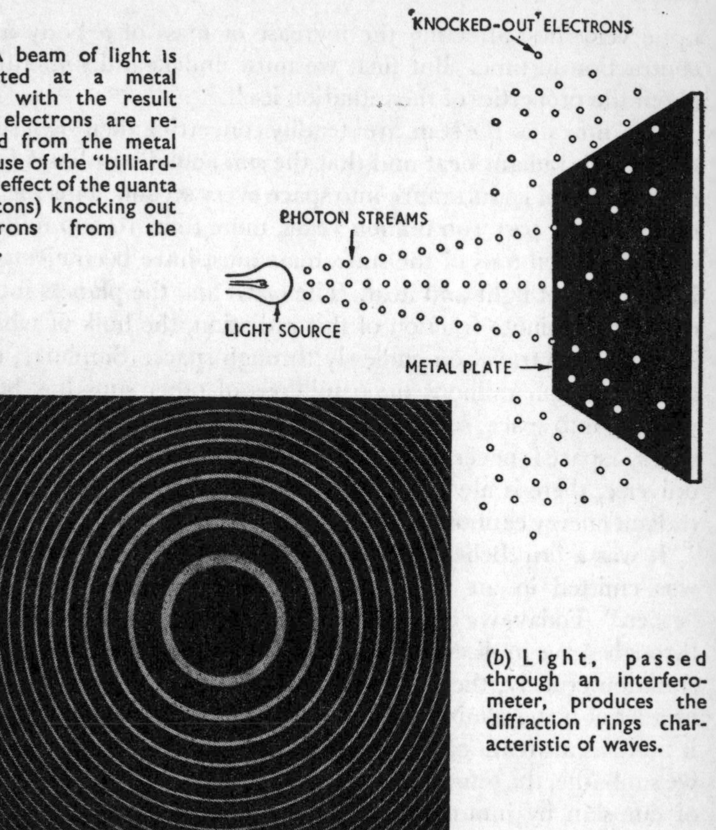

(*a*) A beam of light is directed at a metal plate with the result that electrons are released from the metal because of the "billiard-ball" effect of the quanta (photons) knocking out electrons from the plate.

(*b*) Light, passed through an interferometer, produces the diffraction rings characteristic of waves.

Fig. 45. Particles—or waves? In the experiments illustrated here, light is treated in different ways, with strangely different results.

of electrons is released from the metal (Fig. 45). It is quite impossible to account for this according to the classical wave theory. The effect of the photon bombardment on the electrons in the metal is analogous to the impact of a billiard ball against another; one quantum of radiation hands on its energy to one electron.

And yet, in the same breath, radiant energy can be made to give a convincing demonstration as waves. The simplest example is obtained by passing a beam of light through a pin-hole, whereupon a disc which consists of alternate concentric rings of light and shade is projected. In the laboratory, the wave nature of light has been demonstrated with striking effect (Fig. 45) by means of an interferometer.

So light must consist of waves but, paradoxically, it must also consist of particles. Nor is this strange duality limited to light. For a long time physicists regarded electrons as sub-atomic particles; today, they find it convenient to regard electrons as both (or either) particles or waves. The wave characteristic was confirmed in experiments made in 1927 when a beam of electrons was aimed at a metal crystal, with the result that concentric rings were produced analogous to those obtained by light passing through a pin-hole.

Well, you may ask, what *is* an electron? If it exhibits wave properties, how can we still regard it as a particle which orbits an atomic nucleus? To this question the physicist can merely answer: we picture the electron as a particle when we find it convenient; at other times, we picture it as a wave. *To inquire why the duality exists is like asking why red is red.* The physicist has long since given up treating the electron as a kind of sub-atomic planet, or, in fact, of dealing with it as a particle in any sense at all. If we wish to know where an electron is going and what its speed is—that is to say, if we treat it as a problem of ordinary mechanics—modern physics cannot tell us. It can answer one of our questions but not both at the same time. One can easily compute the details of a planet's motion; its speed and position can be estimated at any time—but to do the same for an electron is quite impossible. The harder you try to keep track of it, the more elusive it becomes. In the words of Bertrand Russell [1] "The more accurately you determine the place of a particle, the less accurate will be its position. And the particle itself has become something quite vague, not a nice little billiard ball as it used to be. When you think you have caught it, it produces a convincing alibi as a wave and not a particle."

With the discovery of the electron's "dual personality," a means was sought of focusing electrons in the same way as a glass lens focuses light. This led to one of the greatest scientific advances of the century—the electron microscope.

[1] "The Greatness of Albert Einstein," *The Listener,* April 28, 1955, p. 746.

One of the drawbacks that had been discovered with the optical microscope was that nothing smaller than the wave-length of visible light (i.e. between 40,000ths to 60,000ths of a centimetre) could be studied. By treating ultra-violet light with special equipment that made it visible, however, the range of observation was brought down to about 100,000ths of a centimetre. But that appeared to be the absolute limit. Beyond this dimension there appeared to be an impenetrable barrier—set by the wave-length of light itself.

The situation which confronted scientists at that time has been likened to the problem of a carpenter cutting square holes of different size with a one-inch chisel. He has no difficulty in producing three-inch holes; he can even cut holes right down to the width of his chisel, but ask him to cut a hole less than one inch wide and he is at once in difficulty; to do the job at all he must resort to a smaller chisel. The scientist's ability to examine smaller objects was limited by the tools available to him; and unless radiation of shorter wave-length could be harnessed for the purpose, further progress seemed impossible.

Thus, with the development of the electron microscope, in which a beam of electrons replaces light, it became possible to study specimens considerably smaller than the wave-length of light; for example, viruses and large molecules (Figs. 23 and 24).

Focused in much the same way as light in an optical microscope, the electron beam is concentrated by specially shaped magnetic fields. In principle, the cathode ray tube of a television set works in a similar way. At the back of the tube, an element is heated which releases a continuous shower of electrons; these electrons are focused into a pencil of rays which strike a fluorescent screen at the flattened end of the tube, appearing as a small spot of light. By applying deflection currents in the magnetic coils situated round the neck of the tube this spot can be made to scan rapidly across the face of the tube. And according to the amount of light and shade in the subject being televised, so the electron beam is automatically modulated, causing the fluorescent crystals in the screen to glow with appropriate

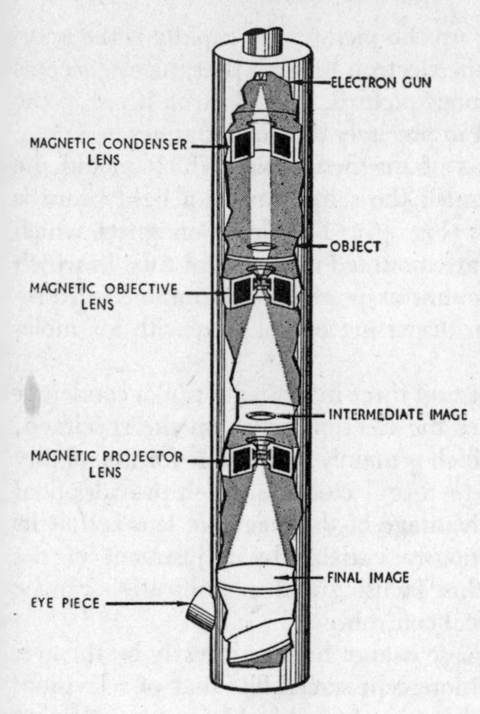

Fig. 46. Electronic and optical microscopes compared. The unaided human eye can resolve objects down to $\frac{1}{4}$ mm. (ovum) ; a good optical microscope $\frac{1}{2000}$ mm. (bacterium) and a modern electronic microscope $\frac{1}{1000000}$ mm. (molecule—containing perhaps 100 to 500 atoms).

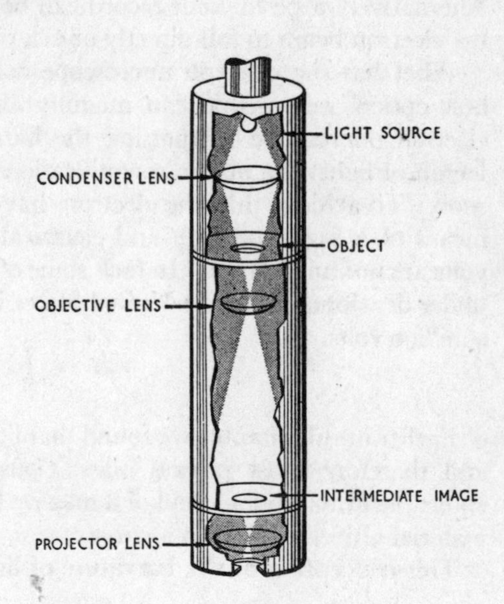

intensity, thus building up the picture. So rapidly is the scanning accomplished by the electron " spot " that the eye accepts the process as a continuous picture. The electron beam in the microscope is produced in precisely the same manner.

The " lenses " consist of magnetic fields which mould the beam of electrons in much the same way as a light beam is moulded by a glass lens (Fig. 46). The electro-magnets, which produce the lens field, are mounted in a vertical tube in which as nearly perfect a vacuum as possible is maintained to prevent the electrons from dispersing by collision with air molecules.

The lens system consists of three main stages : (*a*) a condenser lens, which concentrates the electron beam on the specimen, (*b*) an objective lens, which is mainly responsible for the quality of the final image, and (*c*) a projector lens which provides final magnification. One advantage of the magnetic lens is that its focal length is continuously variable by adjustment of the excitation current, so that focusing and magnification can be varied by simple electrical controls.

Since the electron image cannot be seen directly by the eye, it is projected onto a fluorescent screen like that of television. Alternatively a permanent record can be obtained by allowing the electron beam to fall directly onto a photographic plate.

What has the electron microscope achieved? Whereas the best optical microscope can magnify about 1,500 times, the electron microscope (surpassing the barrier set by the wavelength of light) can obtain magnifications of 80,000 times, and more. To achieve this, the electrons have to be accelerated by means of a high voltage—and electrical pressures of 100,000 volts are not uncommon. In fact, some of the latest instruments under development in the United States will require more than a million volts.

Earlier in this chapter we found that light is a form of energy and therefore must possess mass. Consequently, when light enters the gravitational field of a massive body, it will—like any material object—travel in a curve.

This conception of the curvature of light, which arose from

Einstein's General Theory of Relativity, was first put to test in 1919 when two expeditions set out to observe the solar eclipse in the spring of that year; one of their tasks was to discover whether light actually bent towards the sun. Einstein had suggested that the light from the stars closest to the sun's disc should be deflected inwards, towards the sun, as the starlight passed through the sun's gravitational field. The fact that the stars cannot be seen in daylight made the experiment impossible under normal conditions, and it was Einstein himself who proposed that it should be done during an eclipse. The procedure was simplicity itself. Photographs would be taken of the stars nearest to the darkened face of the sun; then, some time later, photographs would be taken of the same stars at night, when the starlight did not pass through the sun's gravitational field.

When the photographic plates were compared, they showed exactly what Einstein had predicted. Light did not travel in straight lines but was curved according to the nature of the gravitational fields through which it passed. It followed that every astronomical body, planet, star and galaxy, will have its influence upon light, which will amount to a distortion of space around it, rather as an island produces eddies in the sea. The more highly concentrated matter is in the universe, the greater will be the resulting curvature of space. From this it is not difficult to understand, that the total of all the matter in the universe will produce a combined distortion on space so that we have the conception of a universe which is closed in upon itself; a ray of light will travel in a great curve and should, theoretically, return to its point of origin. Attempts have been made to check this effect with America's large telescopes, by looking for the faint image of our own galaxy; theoretically, we should expect to see the image in any direction we cared to look! But then, space would be filled with many such images.

To a world that had been schooled in Euclidean geometry and the rule that the shortest distance between two points is a straight line, the dramatic confirmation of Einstein's theory was a revelation. Only when we construct geometrical figures on a drawing board can we accept Euclid's theorem. Of course, the rule cannot strictly apply on the surface of a globe like the earth. A pilot who wishes to fly to New York from London by the *shortest route* does not set a straight course across the Atlantic but takes a curved path towards Iceland, Newfoundland, and Nova Scotia. Einstein's discovery led to a similar conclusion about the universe. The shortest distance in space is a curve of great circle. And a ray of light will theoretically circumnavigate the universe.

Arising from the same theory were other even more startling conclusions. One is that processes on the sun actually take place more slowly than similar processes on the earth, as a result of the higher surface gravitation. An atom on the sun's surface will emit light at a slightly lower frequency than an atom of the same element on the earth. Actually, the difference is exceedingly small in the case of the sun, but there is one type of star—the so-called White Dwarf—in which the effect is easily measurable. It should be explained that White Dwarf stars represent matter in its most degenerate state. Instead of being huge spheres of incandescent gas, they are tiny bodies no bigger than planets. In fact, the density of a star of this type is just about a million times greater than any solid material found on the earth, so that bare atomic nuclei and free electrons must be packed closely together in the most fantastic state imaginable.

One of these freak stars is the companion of Sirius, a stellar system in which two components revolve round a common centre of gravity. Although this star is only about three times the size of the earth, it is so condensed that one cubic inch of its substance would weigh a ton. Consequently, its massive gravitational field not only perturbs the movement of Sirius, *seventy* times its size, but as the spectroscope has shown, the frequency of the light it emits is effectively reduced. Thus, a ray of light grazing this star would be bent and directed into an entirely different part of space. And as Einstein had also predicted, photons loose a calculable amount of energy in escaping from a gravitational field. This is revealed as a shift of wave-length in the spectrum of the star towards the red.

Arising from this same effect is Einstein's conclusion that had we the ability to place a clock on the surface of the companion of Sirius—and it would have to be an exceptionally robust clock!—it would actually *loose* time with respect to a master clock on the earth. This, of course, would have nothing to do with increased friction on the bearings or any other mechanical feature, but would arise purely as a result of the changed nature of the space-time continuum in which it dwelt, which brings us to yet another important outcome of Einstein's Theory. Though widely different, it will be seen to have surprisingly similar results.

Something has already been said of the question, arising from Einstein's General Theory of Relativity, that no material body can exceed the speed of light. We have learnt too, that peculiar things begin to happen when this enormous speed is approached. Needless to say, the effect is noticeable only when speeds of a high fraction of the speed of light are involved, so that only in the realm of atomic physics can we obtain direct evidence of the phenomenon.

It is well known that the mass of a body determines the force that must be applied to set it in motion; the larger the mass, the more energy will be needed to increase its velocity. Consequently, when Einstein said that no material body could exceed the speed of light, he meant that the resistance of the body to more acceleration (in other words, its *mass*) must increase as it approaches optic velocity. For example, the mass of electrons emitted by radioactive materials with a velocity of 99 per cent that of light is several times that of electrons in a state of rest. In fact, the electrons constituting cosmic rays, which often travel at a velocity of 99·98 per cent that of light, are about 1,000 times as massive. So important is this effect that, as we saw earlier, allowance has to be made for it in the design of particle accelerators.

Towards the end of his life, Einstein was at work on a problem that had baffled him for a quarter of a century. Having arrived at the relationship between matter and energy, he sought the relationship which, he firmly believed, must exist between gravitation and electro-magnetism.

The quest had begun as early as 1919 when, in a technical paper presented to the Prussian Academy of Sciences, the great physicist posed the question: "Do gravitational fields play an important role in the structure of elementary particles of matter?"

In the latter half of the nineteenth century, the experiments of Faraday had revealed a relationship between electricity and magnetism. These experiments had clearly shown that an electric current was surrounded by a magnetic field; and in a reverse manner, that under certain conditions, magnetic forces could be made to induce electrical currents. Was there between electricity and gravitation a similar relationship?

The problem could be summarized thus: Everything in nature has an electrical basis, centred in the electro-magnetic field that binds the atom. The earth, the sun and the other stars, have magnetic fields; and indeed the parallel between the magnetic field of the atomic nucleus and the gravitational field of the sun is very striking.

In the theory he completed in 1949, Einstein set out laws designed to unite these concepts. But the real essence of this final work went much further than gravitation and electro-magnetism. What Einstein sought was to embrace the whole complex of Nature in one unified theory, wherein the macrocosm and the microcosm—the giant wheeling galaxies of cosmic space and the micro-structures of the atom and all their sundry manifestations, would merge. Mass and energy, particles and waves, matter and radiation, electro-magnetism and gravitation—all would be accounted for simply by changes in the structure and density of the primordial field.

That these new concepts in theoretical physics have left an impact can be gauged from the large number of firms and universities which are now engaged in a field of research known as " anti-gravitics."

In 1955, the Americans disclosed that no less than thirty-five electronics and aeronautical companies and a number of universities and research foundations were working on a programme designed to probe the secrets of universal gravitation under the direction of leading American physicists. In addition, one of the aircraft companies, Glenn L. Martin of Baltimore, has signed two of Europe's leading authorities on gravity and electro-magnetism, Dr. Burkhard Heim, Professor of Theoretical Physics of Göttingen University, and Dr. Pascal Jordan of Hamburg University. The Glenn Martin Company has set up between Washington and Baltimore a laboratory called the Research Institute for Advanced Study where a theoretical investigation of the implications of the " unified field theory " of the late Dr. Einstein in future gravity research is now in progress.

What is the meaning of this intense activity in what, after all, is a rather abstract field of study? It is an open secret that, apart from broadening human knowledge generally, research into gravity may lead to revolutionary new aircraft techniques. Several leading aircraft engineers in the United States have voiced their enthusiasm for gravity research. William P. Lear, chairman of Lear Incorporated, one of America's largest electronic firms specializing in aviation, has expressed his conviction that it will be possible to create artificial electro-magnetic fields whose polarity can be controlled to cancel out gravity. These fields, he says, will be adjustable so as to increase or decrease the weight of any object in its surroundings.

Although scientists still know little about gravity and its exact relationship to electro-magnetism, recent nuclear research and experiments with powerful " atom smashers," such as the Cosmotron and Bevatron, are providing a flood of new evidence believed to have a bearing on this. Dr. Stanley Deser and Dr. Richard Arnowitt of the Princeton Institute for Advanced Study have suggested that very recently discovered sub-atomic particles of high-energy, which are difficult to explain by any known theory, may prove to be the key that eventually unlocks the mystery.

CHAPTER SEVEN *The Time Paradox*

" Indeed, life's development, the evolution of awareness, may best be rendered into three attitudes towards Time. Then we see successively the Time-unaware animal, the Time-haunted man, and the Time-understanding mind."

GERALD HEARD.

MODERN MAN'S most important possessions are clocks and calenders. With them, two people can synchronize events with such precision that they meet at a given place at exactly the same time, even though the meeting may have been planned years before. They enable us to organize systems of transport, help us to turn up regularly at our jobs, and allow us to plan all sorts of activities.

Because of the homage we unconsciously pay to them, we have become accustomed to thinking of time as fixed and unchangeable, and of events as flowing around us out of the future and into the past.

As any schoolboy knows, clocks and calenders, in their turn, are geared to the movements of the earth in space. Our planet revolves once on its axis every twenty-four hours and travels once round the sun in 365 days—a day and a year respectively.

It must be remembered, however, that the other planets of our solar system have movements of their own, which differ from those on the earth. If we lived on Mars, a " day " would last twenty-four hours thirty-seven minutes, and a year would be fully 687 days long simply because Mars takes a little longer to revolve on its axis and almost twice as long to complete its orbit round the sun. And on Jupiter, our familiar " year " would be stretched to a period covering nearly twelve earth-years, so long does the giant planet take to complete its orbit; on this reckoning, we should be " old " at the age of six! However, there would be compensation in the fact that a " day "

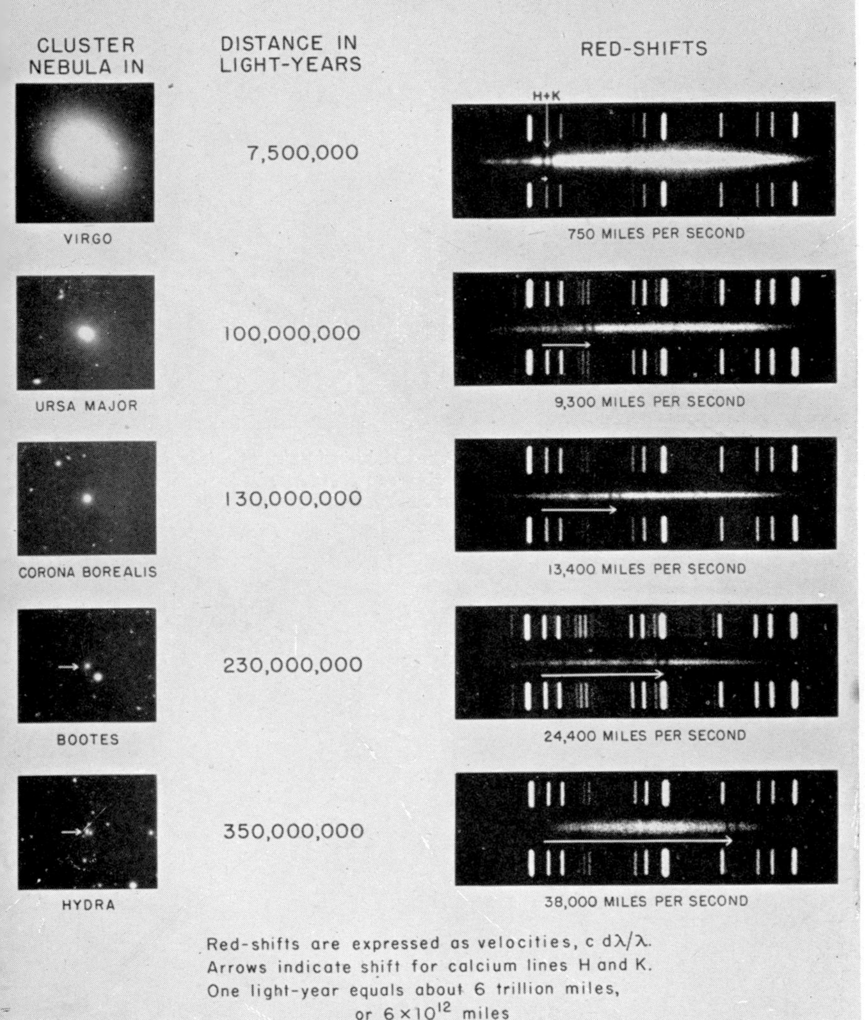

Fig. 47. Diagram explaining the " red shift " theory of the expanding universe. Since this chart was prepared, American astronomers have re-evaluated distance scales, and have approximately doubled the " size " of the observable universe.

Mt. Wilson and Palomar Observatories.

Fig. 48. (1) Crab Nebula in Taurus, seen with the 200-inch telescope, is believed to be the deb of a super-nova, or " exploding star," first recorded by Chinese astronomers in A.D. 1054. powerful emitter of radio signals, the explosion cloud is still expanding at the rate of 680 miles/se

Mt. Wilson and Palomar Observatori

Fig. 49. (2) The giant radio-telescope at Jodrell Bank, Cheshire. With its aid, radio-astronome may listen to " galactic noise " produced more than 2,000 million years ago.

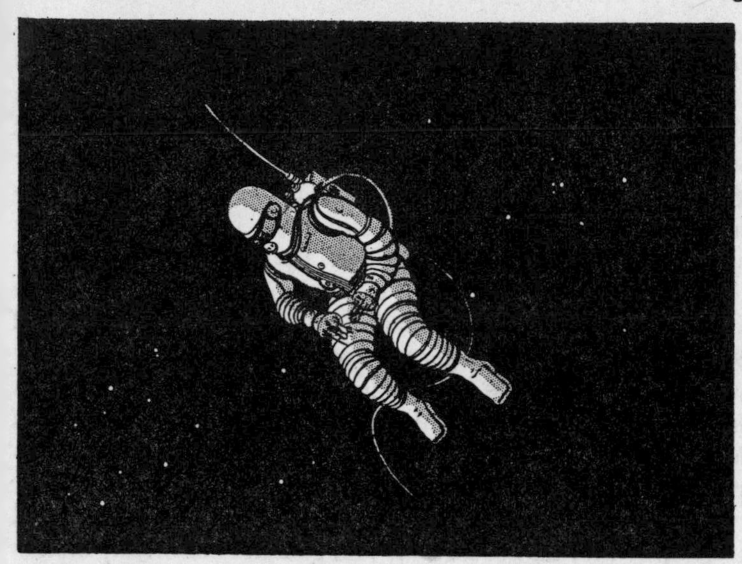

Fig. 50. Should an explorer of the future have the misfortune to lose himself in space, far from the earth or any other planet, time would lose its meaning.

lasts only nine hours fifty-five minutes because of Jupiter's faster rate of spin.

Still greater difficulties will arise if we travel beyond our solar system. Suppose, for example, we could visit another planetary system which, let us say, exists around the double star Sirius. Looking back towards our own sun, we should see a pinpoint of light—but this would not represent the sun as it was at the instant of viewing. In fact, it would be nothing but an image that began its journey across space over eight-and-a-half years before. It would have taken all that time for light, travelling at approximately 186,000 miles per second, to reach us. What is actually seen has no relationship with the time-scale of our immediate surroundings. To an observer in the Sirius system, " now " on the earth would be a moment eight and a half years in the future.

Thus, time is a relative quantity—like speed, a sensation which is very noticeable in an aeroplane flying close to the ground, but which is entirely lost when flying in the stratosphere, when our rate of progress can no longer be compared with stationary objects. Are we, in fact, conscious that we are travelling with a velocity of 66,600 miles per hour as the earth sweeps on its orbit round the sun? Are we at all apprehensive of the fact that our little self-contained world, with the sun and the rest of the solar system, is being carried round the centre of the galaxy at a speed of 600,000 miles an hour? Apart from seemingly unrelated things like the gradual interchange of the seasons, such motions go unnoticed. But should an explorer of the future have the misfortune to lose himself in space, far from the earth or any other planetary body, time (like speed) would lose its meaning. No longer part of a planet that continuously rotates out of darkness into the light of the sun and back again into the shadow, night and day would have no meaning : for as long as the space-man survived, he would live in a continuous present.

Thus, when astronomers peer into space through powerful telescopes, they do not see stars and galaxies but merely images of what these bodies used to be. In probing the depths of space, they are actually looking backwards in time! Sirius is one of the nearest stars and yet so sparsely are the stars scattered that among the twenty *brightest* stars to be seen in the night sky are some whose light takes as long as 500 years to reach us.

But this is not all. If we take the question of time a stage further, into the precincts of Einsteinian physics, we find that time depends upon motion, which brings us again to the famous Theory of Relativity.

One of the chief factors which led Einstein to this Theory was the result of the Michelson-Morley Experiment of 1881 which had been performed to discover to what extent the speed of light was affected by the earth's motion. A small difference in consequence of the earth's motion through the ether was expected, with a small but detectable increase in velocity in one direction and an equally small decrease in the other.

The substance of the argument is briefly this : The speed of a ship through a calm sea cannot be determined by any experiment performed within the ship, but only with reference to the sea itself. For example, if a log is thrown overboard, the rate at which the log falls astern will disclose the speed of the ship through the sea.

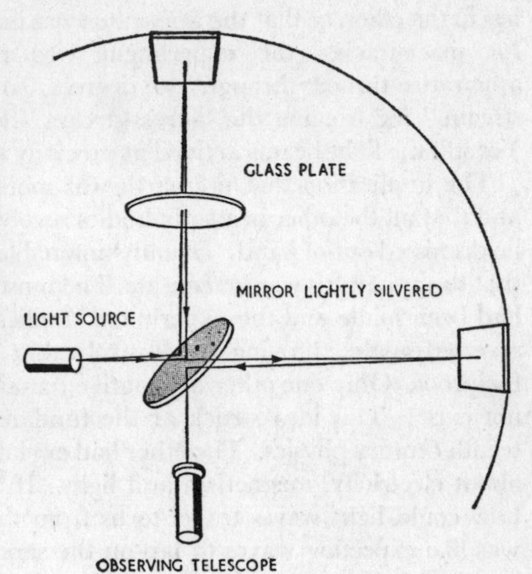

Fig. 51. The Michelson-Morley Experiment (first performed in 1881). Light is directed on to a half-silvered mirror A so that part of the beam is reflected along A–B and the rest continues along A–C (both distances being of equal length). Mirrors at B and C reflect the light back to A and half of each beam passes into a small telescope, where the results are compared.

A similar reasoning lay behind the Michelson-Morley Experiment. The earth was the ship travelling through the ether sea, and a light signal was the " log " that was thrown overboard.

If the earth was moving through the ether (as observations had shown it was) then the double journey of the light beam first from E to W and then from W to E, should take slightly longer than one of equal length from N to S and S to N. This was like expecting two oarsmen of equal speed, one rowing a certain distance *upstream and downstram*, and the other rowing an equal distance *across stream* to arrive at different times. In fact, the cross-stream oarsman will always arrive first because the gain in time in rowing with the current will never be sufficient to compensate for the time lost in rowing against the current. The difference in time between the two boats will reveal the speed of the current. Logically, in the Michelson-Morley Experiment it was expected that the time lag between the two light beams would reveal the earth's speed through the ether. But the result was against all common sense. It proved conclusively that, despite what happens in the case of oarsmen, light beams have *equal transit times*. It meant either that the earth was motionless in the ether, or that the apparatus was inaccurate. To check for inaccuracies, the experiment was repeated with the apparatus turned through 90 degrees, so that the " downstream " leg became the " cross-stream " leg, and *vice versa.* Yet still the light beams arrived at precisely the same instant.

The implication that the earth was motionless in the ether, and that all the other heavenly bodies revolved around it, could be dismissed out of hand. Equally untenable was the suggestion that the apparatus was inaccurate. The most painstaking checks had been made and the experiment duplicated many times at reversed angles, proving conclusively that the apparatus was foolproof. Only one other alternative remained—the ether did not exist! This idea struck at the fundamentals of the nineteenth century physics. The ether had explained so many things about electricity, magnetism and light. If there was no ether, how could light waves travel to us from the distant stars? It was like expecting waves to lap on the shore without water to sustain them!

The problem threw scientific thought into confusion for a quarter of a century. It took a genius to resolve the dilemma.

It was not until Einstein published his Special Theory of Relativity in 1905 that the apparent contradiction between classical physics and the constancy of the speed of light under all conditions of observation was resolved. It is impossible to give a convincing explanation of the Theory without considerable mathematics and here we must content ourselves with a generalized discussion of how the Theory affects our view of the universe.

The overriding truth of the matter is that the speed of light is constant regardless of the earth's motion. Whereas a bullet fired from the front of a moving train will have a speed which is the sum of the two speeds, a ray of light projected in the direction of the earth's motion will only travel at light speed; the speed of the earth can be ignored. Thus, science was left with the paradox that one train travelling behind another at a fixed speed will never join, but a ray of light or a wireless wave travelling in the direction of a hypothetical space ship moving at the speed of light will overhaul the space ship at precisely light speed. In other words, the problem can be treated exactly as if the signal were being transmitted between two *fixed* stations.

The Special Theory had two other implications which, like the constancy of the speed of light, seemed to be against all common sense. One was that mass and energy are interchangeable according to a simple mathematical relationship[1]; the other, that the mass of a body increases with its velocity.[2]

Few people today will deny the validity of Einstein's first assumption, the conversion of matter into energy having been demonstrated only too dramatically in our time! But the second part of the Theory, that mass increases with speed, is not so readily appreciated, despite the fact that it too has been verified experimentally.

At speeds within the range of common experience, including those of astronomical bodies, the difference in mass is negligible. Indeed, it is only when we consider atomic particles with speeds of a high fraction of the speed of light that the results become really apparent.

For example, the effect has been observed with electrons and allowance has to be made for this in the design of cyclotrons which are used to accelerate these particles in order to give them the sufficiently high energies required for atomic bombardment. As a particle approaches optic velocity, its mass increases sensationally and adjustment has to be made in the apparatus. According to the relativistic laws of dynamics, no body can ever exceed the speed of light because it would possess infinite mass; and the total annihilation of all the matter in the universe would not suffice to accelerate it further.

Increase in mass is not the only sensational result of travel at near-optic velocities. Einstein's view was that since all bodies in the universe have their own particular motion, each must have a different time. Again, the time-variation will be small in the case of astronomical bodies but, like the interrelation of mass

[1] $E = MC^2$

[2] $M = \dfrac{M_0}{\sqrt{1 - \dfrac{V^2}{C^2}}}$

and energy and the increase of mass with speed, the effect has been demonstrated in atomic physics.

Confirmation of the theory was obtained as the result of work into the behaviour of cosmic radiation. It has been found that the bombardment of oxygen and nitrogen nuclei in the atmosphere by cosmic ray primaries (having velocities of 0·9995 that of light) produces very high energy particles called *mesons.* The average life of these mesons at rest is two-millionths of a second, and at the speed of light, the distance covered in this time would be approximately four-tenths of a mile. The average height at which these mesons are produced is ten miles, and therefore if the average distance traversed were only four-tenths of a mile, the proportion of mesons arriving at the earth's surface would be immeasurably small. In fact, a large proportion reach the surface, which can only be explained if we assume that the time-dilation effect experienced by the meson has the effect of lengthening its life.

To discover what this means in more familiar terms, let us consider the case of a hypothetical train travelling at a high fraction of the speed of light. For the moment, let us imagine that we are the observers waiting on the platform of a station somewhere along the track. If we can now look in upon the travellers on this train, as it passes, we shall be conscious of some very strange happenings indeed. For one thing, the passengers are queerly flattened in the direction of motion, like figures cut out of cardboard. There are long intervals between their heartbeats, and respiration extends over a long interval. The tick of the clock on the carriage wall is equally slow, its time far behind that of the clock on the station platform. The train itself is a mere fraction of the length it should be. Such is the fragmentary impression that greets us from the platform.

But meanwhile, as it thunders past at fantastic speed, let us switch the scene to the train itself and see what the passengers make of their strange plight. To our great surprise, they appear indifferent to what has occurred. They read and exchange glances like normal travellers and appear to see no difference in their surroundings; to each other, they are quite ordinary three-dimensional people travelling in an ordinary three dimensional train. A portly businessman checks his wristwatch with the clock in the carriage; yes, the train is on schedule, he won't be late for his appointment. He resumes his corner seat, and casually lets up the window-blind. Suddenly, his attention is riveted on something outside. What on earth was wrong with the station that just flashed past? Wasn't it strangely squashed? And weren't those people standing on the platform horribly thin? Could he be dreaming? Rather dazed, he struggles to his feet clutching his bottle of pills and disappears unsteadily towards the dining car.

In this little episode, we have the full impact of the term "relativity." Observers in different circumstances will not agree. And time is not a universal constant.

All astronomical bodies possess their own particular time-scales and these will differ according to their velocities. The effect may not be measurable in terms of motions with which we are ordinarily familiar, but it could exist for a space ship travelling close to the speed of light. And yet the crew of such a space ship would experience nothing of these strange happenings because they and their surroundings would be changed uniformly. The watch on the skipper's wrist will still read the same as the clock on the wall of the cabin. But if, in some way, it could be checked with a clock on the earth, the two would not agree. And all the scientific checks that could be made of the clock on the earth and the clock in the space ship would suggest that *both were correct*, despite the fact that *they show different times*. This is the "Alice in Wonderland" universe that Einstein reveals to us—a universe of strange contradictions, where 2 and 2 make anything but 4.

Nature, always economical, has given us eyes which are sensitive to a very limited range of radiations; she has also given us senses which give logical results only so long as we limit our reasoning to the conditions under which we were born.

The deeper we go into these relativistic effects, the farther we get from classical physics and the less we can rely upon personal observation. It is as though our solar system were part of a separate universe, with distinct laws that apply only so long as we limit ourselves to the realm of common experience. However, to imagine that under totally different conditions, at tremendous speeds of motion and over vast astronomical distances, everything should proceed in precisely the way we expect on the earth, is merely human conceit. At the furthest reach of scientific inquiry, the electron is observed to behave both as a particle and as a wave; mass increases with speed and time is not a universal constant. But these things need not disturb us. Paradox arises only when we limit our thinking to the singular environment into which we were born.

After all, common experience teaches us to judge the size of a man whether he is far away and appears " small," or close-up, when he assumes his true stature. We do not have to think about it; we accept the phenomenon without demanding proof that it is so because it is part of our everyday experience.

If we were accustomed to bodies travelling at near-optic velocities, whose mass increases with speed, we should accept this as unthinkingly as we accept the apparent change in the size of a man. And just as readily, we should accept the time-dilation effect that goes with it!

If time is an illusion, how does this hypothesis fit in with the physical universe of which we, on this earth, are so minute a part? One might well inquire: " How did it all begin? " For one thing, if we cannot depend on time, can we logically expect to find a fixed point at which the universe was brought into being?

Our great problem is that we are accustomed to finding solutions which can immediately be grasped in three-dimensional terms. " Man came from monkey " (though it is not scientifically true) is something most people can readily appreciate. " God created Man " is altogether different because God cannot be interpreted in anything but abstract terms.

Earlier, we saw that matter consists of aggregations of atomic particles which are transparent to other atomic particles. A stone, a drop of water, a blade of grass, the air around us—all these things are constituted of spinning worlds of agitated particles having little mass but enormous stores of potential energy. It is hard to think of these particles as being almost all empty space, and it is perhaps harder still to think of ourselves as being constructed of the same quivering and dancing atoms. So if we wish to know something about how the universe began, we must keep firmly in mind this atomic picture of the " material " world.

In a previous chapter we saw that matter (form) and energy (force) are dualistic; under varying circumstances, energy can manifest as matter and matter can manifest as energy. The steady conversion of hydrogen into helium which is going on continuously in the stars produces a dispersion of matter in the form of (radiant) energy. Conversely, there is the continuous harnessing of energy in form (matter) which has led upward to the familiar chemical and biological developments of our world. It is therefore pertinent to inquire how the energy that drives the universe originated.

Our last material clue to this momentous question is the evidence we have that the universe is composed predominantly of hydrogen gas. How, then, did the primordial hydrogen atom enter the picture to begin this incredible story of the " physical universe? "

Any discussion along these lines must be the result of a purely personal exploration; and unlike our scientific studies, it will be impossible to offer proof. However, this state of affairs is not entirely unknown even to science, for in his investigations into the ultimate particles of the atom, the nuclear physicist is no longer demanding a proof of his discoveries. He has learnt a lot about the atom without ever seeing it! In fact, the closer he peers into the atom the vaguer his impressions become.

Have you ever dreamt that something was within your grasp and yet all your efforts to catch and hold it were in vain? Have you almost caught hold of that elusive something and found it somewhere else, behind you, ahead of you—anywhere, in fact, but where you thought it was? Have you found it to dissolve almost as your fingers closed around it? That is no dream to the physicist; *it is an ever present reality*! " . . . it is impossible to know at one instant the position and velocity of even one single particle," writes Professor Andrade.[1] " It is not a question of improving instruments—the thing is unknowable. Science has become very modest!" Yes, a great deal of our knowledge about the atom we must accept on faith!

The question we must strive to answer is whether the universe is purposive. That is to say, has man emerged from the shapeless dust clouds of interstellar space merely as the result of blind throws of chance, or is there some special kind of direction behind it all?

What can one say about an evolutionary process that has taken a tenuous cloud of gas and created a living being as complex as man, with all his vain hopes and desires, his courage and daring, his greed and jealousy—his poetry and art and yet, in the same breath, a creature unique in his own experience capable of questioning the meaning and purpose of his existence? Is this a meaningless story of the blind groping of chemical reactions; or is it instead one of infinite and magnificent purpose?

Summarizing the extent of our knowledge so far, we have the evidence that matter and energy are dualistic, and also that the primary constituent of the universe is hydrogen. We have as an analogy a picture of the universe as a soap bubble which is constantly expanding. But what analogy can we find for its origin? The theory of " continuous creation " is one that satisfies most of our difficulties concerning the structure of the universe, but the question mark it poses is immense. " At one moment the atoms of hydrogen do not exist, and at a later time they do," Hoyle writes. This does not imply that the power that drives the universe is a " closed-cycle," energy building into matter and matter reverting to energy. If the universe is expanding and, *at the same time, maintaining its density*, the amount of " material " it contains must be for ever increasing. However one may look at it, it is difficult to escape the conclusion that energy is entering the universe—as we say in conventional language—" from some external source."

If we accept the hypotheses of " continuous creation," we at once dispose of the idea that the substance of the universe came

[1] " The Uncertainty Principle," Professor E. N. da C. Andrade, F.R.S., *The Listener*, July 10, 1947.

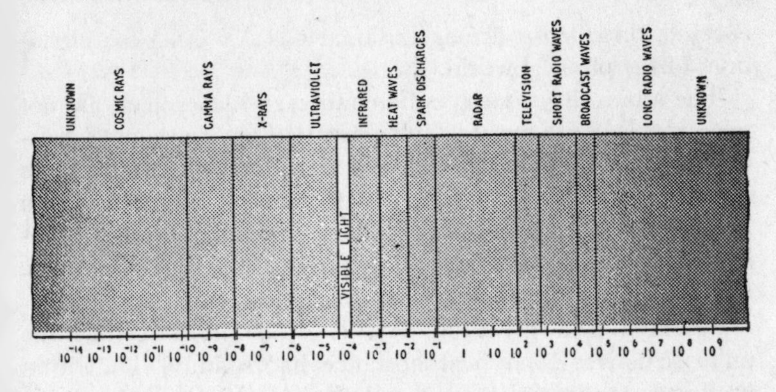

Fig. 52. The electro-magnetic spectrum.

into being at some fixed time in the past and that it is moving towards decay. Instead we have a virile, ever developing universe of immense potentiality.

Where do these hydrogen atoms come from? What is meant by " out of nowhere "?

To go further into this intriguing question, we must first consider the narrow confines of the " window " through which we gain our impressions of the universe. The particular " window " we depend upon most is the " optical window " (Fig. 52), an extremely small section of the known spectrum. All other impressions outside this narrow band are shuttered and barred to our senses and only by means of instruments have we been able to break down this barrier and discover the existence of radiation other than visible light (e.g. X-rays, infra-red and cosmic rays). Consider, for a moment, what it would be like if our eyes were not tuned to this small waveband in the visible spectrum, but instead were responsive only to X-rays. Or suppose we could only " see " in infra-red. How different the universe would appear then, and what different ideas we should have concerning its nature! The universe would take on an entirely different character for each kind of " seeing."

This idea illustrates perhaps better than any other how limited is the consciousness that judges all things on the basis of what it can see and feel. And yet, as we have already discovered, these senses are as illusionary as any other manifestations of the physical world.

The atoms that compose the chair on which you sit are not microscopic bits of matter, but energy without any known structure. In fact, the more we seek to understand the atom the more its secrets shrink from us. It has been described as a solar system in miniature—a number of negatively charged electrons revolving round a positive charge of electricity, the proton-nucleus. Yet no one has ever told us what an electron is!

The atom is the great paradox. It is the unit from which the universe derives its physical substance, its " solidity," but within itself it is non-material, for the " particles " in its make-up do not appear to consist of anything tangible in the physical sense. Yet there is no denying the fantastic store of energy that is locked up in these discrete particles—*energy which we have seen is able to build as well as to destroy.*

It is through the ability of atoms to unite and modify among themselves that the universe and man himself have been fashioned from the nebulous clouds of hydrogen gas that permeate space. Thus we return to the question: " Whence came the hydrogen atom? " It simply appears, says Hoyle: at one moment the atom does not exist and the next moment it does; such atoms are in the process of being created throughout the universe. It means that creation did not occur at some fixed time in the past but that creation is going on around us at all times.

On the whole, scientists like to deal with things they can measure. They do not like " untidy " theories which introduce assumptions that are beyond the immediate province of scientific analysis. They are much happier dealing with tidy dynamic laws.

Consequently, when it is suggested that atoms are in the process of being continually created throughout the universe, in the eyes of many scientists this is tantamount to cheating and something to be abhorred. It is much wiser, they say, to deal with things that can be observed and proven without introducing such grand (and convenient) assumptions; all of which is very fine if we are merely intent upon keeping our sums neat and tidy. But, in fact, have we not displaced the problem?

Consider the alternative, which has the approval of many astronomers. Instead of a creation in which matter is continually emerging in the universe, creation occurred at a fixed time in the past, when all the matter of the universe was suddenly brought into being. Instead of originating continuously from "nowhere," it originated explosively from "nowhere."

So, whichever term we choose, we must start with that perplexing term "out of nowhere." In the one case, *continuous creation* is responsible for the universe; in the other, it was a *primordial explosion.* It may all have happened within a microsecond, or it may be spread over all eternity; but in either hypothesis, the atoms comprising the universe came (or come) from "nowhere."

To our senses, bounded as they are by a three-dimensional consciousness, the mind boggles at the suggestion of continuous creation. Does this mean that there is some source of energy outside the physical universe?

How does the theory of continuous creation fit in with Einstein's conception of an expanding universe which is "finite but unbounded"? If it is finite, then its volume is limited; but if at the same time it is unbounded, the only way we can conceive it in a model is as a sphere (Chapter Four). And if we accept Hoyle's premise that the universe is both expanding and maintaining its density, we have the conception of three-dimensional space swelling into "nothingness." We arrive at the same intangible stage we have previously reached in our study of the atom—the stage where no further physical investigation is possible.

How, then, can we pursue the question? We can do so only by casting off the familiar world of three dimensions.

CHAPTER EIGHT *Other Universes*

" There is no death of a thing, except in appearance; and so, also there is no birth of anything, except in appearance. That which passes from essence into nature, seems to be birth, and what passes from nature into essence seems, in like manner to be death; though nothing really is originated, and nothing ever perishes; but only now comes into sight, and now vanishes. It appears by reason of the density of matter, and disappears by reason of the tenuity of essence; but is always the same, differing only in motion and condition."

APOLLONIUS OF TYANA.

LET US step through the looking-glass into a " Wonderland " in which only two dimensions exist. Call it " Flatland." It is a strange world in which the inhabitants are as shadows possessing only length and breadth. However, these creatures are highly intelligent but since their entire experience is limited to Flatland, they possess no knowledge whatever of any dimensions beyond their own. Lacking any conception of " height " they can neither rise nor fall; nor can they even *think* of doing so! Our model of this mythical world would be a vast sheet of paper without undulations or ridges.

Now consider what would happen if a sphere (representing our three-dimensional world) were to descend upon the plane of Flatland and pass through it (Fig. 62). Lacking any conception of three-dimensional space, the inhabitants of Flatland would not see the approaching sphere, nor could they have any idea of its solidity; they would be aware only of the impression of a circle which grows from a point as the sphere cuts the plane of Flatland, driving them outwards from its circumference. The circle would continue to expand until half the sphere had passed through the plane of Flatland, when the circle would begin to contract, diminishing again to a point and vanishing as the sphere departed.

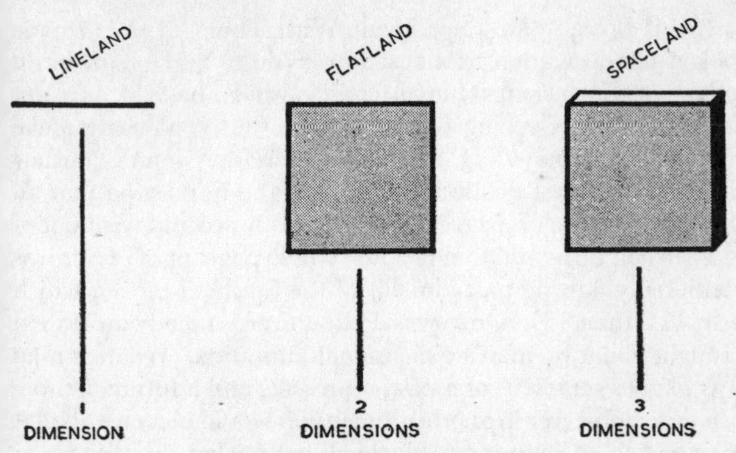

Fig. 53. Simple dimensional concepts.

How would the Flatlanders regard this phenomenon? No doubt many would regard it as a kind of miracle, perhaps a portent of some disaster, but the " Einsteins " of Flatland would have a number of ingenious theories, though none of them would have any chance of comprehending the truth. They would be able to measure the rate at which the circle expanded and contracted and would mistakenly attribute to *growth in time* what the more privileged observer in three-dimensions ascribes to *solidity and motion*.

In this little analogy, we have a method of dealing with all the things we find " intangible " to our three-dimensional consciousness—the nature of the electron, the expanding universe, and the idea of a continuous creation.

Keeping in mind the Flatlanders' predicament, let us now consider the movement of a fourth-dimension through three-dimensional space. In this four-dimensional existence, the past and the future are all depicted and are fully discernible to the consciousness of a four-dimensional being. If there is motion of four-dimensional space relative to the third dimension of our common experience, all the changes we experience and attribute to the passage of time will be due to this movement, whereas the whole of the future as well as the past always exist. In fact, it is only in the lower dimension that " past " and " present " have any meaning!

In his book, " An Experiment With Time," J. W. Dunne looked upon creation as a vast forest of life and events in an unknown dimension. Human consciousness, he said, was not capable of experiencing this as a whole but could only make contact with one thing at once. Therefore, man's journey through the forest of life left him with the impression that all the various trees, or events, came into existence and went out of existence in turn—that, in fact, the whole pageant of events was continually flowing past him out of the future, a process which he calls " time." Dunne suggested that time is merely an illusion brought about by man's dimensional limitation. Whereas man was plainly conscious of a past, a present, and a future, a more privileged observer in another dimension would perceive all that man had to encounter as a single all-embracing experience.

Along the corridor of time dinosaurs still roam, the pyramids are being built and the first men are leaving for the moon. In this situation, man is in much the same position as the " Flatlander " who saw a circle which, in fact, was a sphere.

Dunne went even further and suggested that sleep provides the human consciousness with the faculty of breaking down the barrier of time and of moving back and forth along the corridor which, in our waking hours, we should regard as the past and the future. In this way, he suggests how it is possible to dream of events which, in real life, are yet to happen.

Apparently, the sensation of withdrawing from the chamber of the present into the " corridor of time " can be produced artificially with a particular range of drugs known as " psychotomimetics."

Foremost exponent in their experimental use is Dr. Humphrey Osmond, Medical Superintendent of a mental hospital in Saskatchewan, who has administered them in his search for a cure for schizophrenics.

Outside medical considerations, Dr. Osmond believes that certain drugs can inhibit the parts of the brain which act as a " filter," and widen our perceptive wave-band to experience the outside world more nearly as it really is before our intellect imposes its pattern upon it.

Fascinated by the results of this research, Aldous Huxley submitted himself to a mescalin experiment which he described in

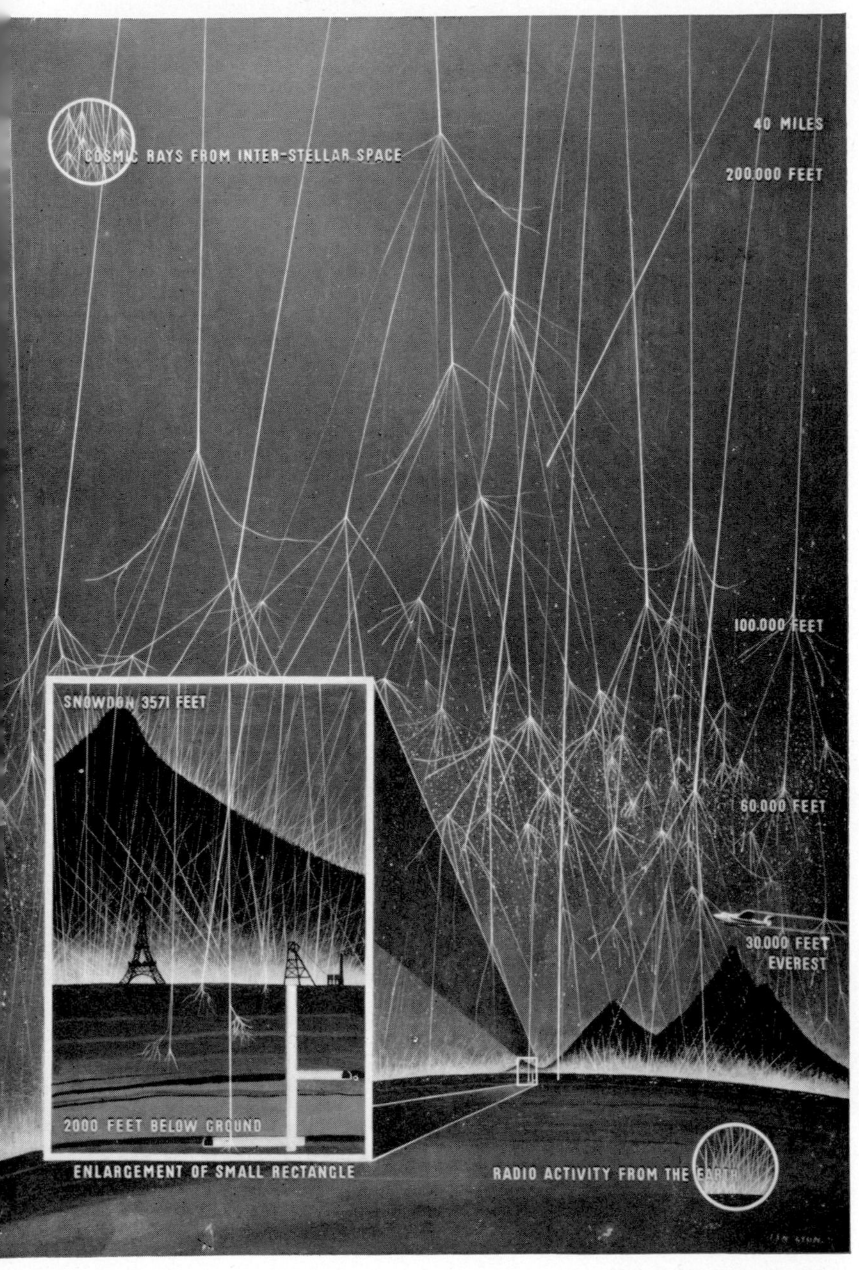

'ig. 54. Diagram illustrating the penetrative power of cosmic rays. This highly energetic radia-ion, whose source still defies solution, can penetrate many feet of lead and has been detected in coal mines 2,000 feet below ground.

Fig. 55. The atom is mostly empty space. If the assemblage of neutrons (white) and prot (black) in the nucleus was the size of a golf-ball, the distance across the atom would be about o third of a mile. An atom of the metal sodium is represented in the model.

remarkable detail in his book " The Doors of Perception."

Since this experiment, Dr. Osmond has administered the drug to a number of interested people whose experiences have varied widely. But overall the sense of timelessness and an interchange of events which vary between the subject and the observer are very much in evidence.

Among those who have submitted themselves to such tests is Christopher Mayhew, M.P., whose experience was filmed and tape-recorded for television, which, however, was never broadcast. Describing his sensations in *The Observer* later, he said : " I was not experiencing the events in the normal sequence of time. I was experiencing the events of 3.30 before the events of 3.0; the events of 2.0 after the events of 2.45, and so on. Several events I experienced with an equal degree of reality more than once.

" I am not suggesting, of course, that the events of 3.30 *happened* before the events of 3.0, or that any events *happened* more than once. All I am saying is that I experienced them, not in the familiar sequence of clock time, but in a different, apparently capricious sequence which was outside my control.

" By ' I ' in this context I mean, of course, my disembodied self, and by ' experienced ' I mean learned by a special kind of awareness which seemed to comprehend yet be different from, seeing, hearing, etc.

" In films, ' flashbacks ' transpose us backwards and forwards in time. We find events of 1956 being suddenly interrupted by events of 1939. In the same way I found later events in our drawing-room—events in which I myself was participating at the bodily level—being interrupted by earlier events and *vice versa*.

" I count this experience, which occurred when, as I say, I was wide awake and intelligent, sitting in my own arm-chair at home, as the most astounding and thought-provoking of my life."

Explaining his interpretation of the experience, Mayhew suggested that from his own peculiar disembodied standpoint, all events in his drawing-room existed together at the same time. It was, of course, a terribly difficult idea to grasp; but it was not, despite appearances, self-contradictory. He then drew these analogies.

" When we take off from an airport at night, we are aware of individual runway lights flashing past in succession. But when we look down a little later, we see them all existing together motionless. It is not self contradictory to say that the lights flash past in succession and also that they exist together motionless. Everything depends on the standpoint of the observer.

" Or take an analogy from reading. When we read something, we are aware of one word coming after another. But when we detach our minds from the sense of the words and look at the page as a whole, this impression fades, and we are aware that the words all exist together at the same time.

" Moreover, with our minds thus detached, our eyes are free to travel over the page in any direction. We can read later words before earlier ones if we wish. But as soon as we start reading again, we automatically become blind to words which lie ahead of us or behind us."

Mescalin does not have the same effect on everyone who takes it. Some people have been known to become suicidal, or have absurd and terrifying hallucinations. Others have burst into uncontrollable fits of laughter. But from all accounts it would appear that the basic patterns of mental behaviour act as a vision projector.

For instance, a Christian would encounter Jesus Christ, the Virgin Mary or his favourite saint; a Mohammedan, on the other hand, would meet the Prophet; and a Buddhist, the Gautama.

That these reactions are produced by the subconscious mind seems to have been confirmed by Mayhew who enjoyed " vast areas of bliss " and attributed this to the fact that he had been studying religious experience and had even hinted before his own experiment that they were theoretically possible.

There is, of course, no need to take drugs to achieve the " timeless " state of mind; hypnosis, yoga, fasting, meditation and prayer will provide it. But whereas with mescalin the state is achieved in a comparatively short time, most of the other methods demand painstaking, hard work, perseverance and patience.

At this point it is intriguing to ask whether this " timeless phenomenon " is related in any way to the " miracle cures " of Lourdes in which hundreds, if not thousands, of tragically afflicted people have suddenly felt in themselves all the symptoms of radiance and perfect health—and yet whose bodies have not manifested the improvement until the normal physical healing time had elapsed? The classic case of Marie Biré who suffered agonizing headaches and dizziness until she went blind as a result of her optic nerve wasting away completely indicates that there could well be!

Describing the case in her book " The Mystery of Lourdes,"[1] Ruth Cranston writes that some months after she had been stricken with blindness, Madame Biré went to Lourdes accompanied by her doctor and her eldest daughter. During a visit to the Grotto where the Virgin Mary is said to have appeared to the 14-year-old peasant girl, Bernadette Soubirous, on February 11, 1858, she suddenly stood up in her invalid carriage and cried: " Ah, I see the Blessed Virgin!" She fell back into her seat, fainting. Her daughter thought she was dying, but she quickly recovered consciousness and found she could actually see.

Among the doctors at the Medical Bureau who examined her was Doctor Henri Lainey, an occulist from Rouen, who wrote: " Examination of the eyes with the ophthalmascope showed both sides a white pearly papilla, devoid of all colour. The diagnosis was forced upon me: here was white atrophy of the optic nerve, of cerebral cause. This, one of the gravest afflictions, is recognized by all authorities as incurable. But Madame Biré could read the finest print, and her distant vision was just as good."

She recovered her sight, but the lesions remained. They were to disappear later.

Ten doctors made a second examination on the following day. The results were the same: the organ was still atrophied and lifeless; the sight was still perfect.

A month after her return home, three eye specialists examined Marie Biré again. The Medical Bureau found that the phenomenon had ceased. The cure was complete. Twenty years later

[1] Evans Brothers Ltd., London. 18/-

her sight was still excellent. The doctors' verdict: "Absolutely inexplicable clinically."

Is it possible that in some way and without knowing it Marie Biré became "depersonalized" as Mayhew described it; depersonalized in a limited way—that is, partially detached to see, not through her physical eyes, but through the mind's "eye," until her own eyes returned to normal in a way we do not yet fully understand?

But then, what about the instantaneous and almost instantaneous cures of Lourdes which still baffle the medical profession?

There is the case of Madame Augustine Augault who had suffered from a fibroid tumour of the uterus for twelve years. She was at death's door when she went to Lourdes and had to be given four injections to help her heart on the journey to the shrine. A doctor who saw her on the train was startled by the dimensions of her abdomen.

On the first morning at Lourdes she was taken to the baths on a stretcher. For the brief instant she was in the water she felt excruciating pain; then the pressure on the abdomen seemed to disappear. She continued to suffer terribly, however, until she was carried to the procession that forms part of the afternoon ceremonial in the little Pyrénéean town. Then at the exact moment the Blessed Sacrament passed by, her sufferings vanished, and she became conscious of renewed energy within herself. Next day, the pool attendants who had bathed her were amazed to see her abdomen quite flat and back to normal. Moreover she was able to walk. It was a permanent cure.

The Medical Bureau at Lourdes has fairly complete records of more than 1,200 cures which have been classified as "inexplicable under scientific and natural laws" and a further 4,000 cases which are probably genuine cures.

Dr. Smiley Blanton, a visiting American physician invited to direct the examination of one of Lourdes most famous cures —Charles McDonald who, after fifteen months immobility and pain with tuberculosis of the spine, nephritis and tubercular arthritis, got out of bed and dressed himself on the third day of his pilgrimage—said: ". . . there does appear to be at this shrine a sudden quickening of the healing processes. The percentages of such cures are too great to be laid to coincidence, nor do the details of the cures conform to the laws of recovery as we know them. Even coincidental cures in our hospitals do not in the space of two or three days get up and walk without pain after fifteen months in bed with continual pain. I believe that something does occur '*which is on the margin of the laws of nature*'."

What is it that causes the sudden healing of malignant tissue and the restoration of wasted nerves?

Does prayer and faith perpetually going up as one voice or thought from the tightly packed mass of friends and relatives on the stands around the sick constitute an almost living force whose rhythms envelop the individual? The answer exists beyond the frontiers of our scientific knowledge.

Dr. Rolf Alexander, author of "The Power of the Mind," who has reduced the rituals of many primitive peoples, the practices of the yogas and the Tibetan monks, to fundamentals, in more than forty years of neurological research, has suggested that we are part of an all-enveloping "over-soul" or immeasurable mind which pervades the physical gases of space; a power that, correctly organized and harnessed by the individual, can work "miracles."

Belief in the magical power of the human will to achieve physical results is at once the most deeply rooted and widespread of all our instinctive beliefs. The "Rain Dances" of the American Indians of the Southwestern Desert, the "Corn Dances" of the Mexican Indians to insure a good harvest; the "Maori Haka" to bring success in war; the various Dervish dances; the voodoo rituals of the Caribs and the cheering of a crowd for a horse, a football team or a boxer . . . all these are perhaps instinctive ways of using one's influence in what has come to be known as "psychokinesis."

During the past century a number of groups of trained investigators in Britain, America and Europe, have looked into thousands of cases of psychic phenomena. Dr. J. B. Rhine's experiments in extrasensory perception at Duke University in the United States are well known: so is the work of Dr. S. G. Soal in Britain. However, the difficulties involved in the psychological approach to an explanation of psychic phenomena are so numerous that it is difficult to say whether any worthwhile progress can be made at the moment. Each subject presents individual problems because his religious and educational conditioning, health, personality and many other elements enter into a complex of factors which cloud the issue.

Dr. Alexander's experiments have demonstrated that although the human brain can trigger a response in this unknown field, in the same manner perhaps as a radio transmitter can trigger a response in the electro-magnetic field, the energy itself is "extra-biological," existing quite independently of the human nervous system as a physical reality, just as the electromagnetic field exists independently of the radio transmitters and receivers which use it.

With the electroencephalograph, neurologists have been able to identify and classify the main electrical rhythms of the human brain and agree that they seem to function behind the frontal lobes. Electrical activity cannot be detected about the fore part of the brain however, and for this reason it is called the "silent area." Yet when the fibres which connect this part of the brain to the rest of it are severed, as in a leucotomy operation, a remarkable change takes place in the person's personality. It would seem therefore, that all our attributes of imagination, will and intuition, reside in this "silent area."

According to Rolf Alexander, his experiments show that the "silent area" is where psychokinetic transmission takes place. So it would seem that although the frontal part of the brain is "silent" in terms of electro-magnetic energy, it is anything but "silent" in terms of the unknown energy.

Now, disregarding the mysterious "psyche" for the moment, the human organism, like every other organism in nature, might be regarded as a collecting, collating and energy distributing machine, and just as the gravitational energy of a waterfall is used to operate a generator for producing electric current, it is possible that the bio-electrical current produced by the human nervous system is used to generate this higher-level energy.

Many psychologists today do not entirely dismiss telepathic communication. If it does occur it is quite certain that the communication from mind to mind is not made through the electro-magnetic field. Because of the extremely small amount of energy involved in even the most pronounced of the brain rhythms, and the very low frequencies of the latter, they would fall below the level of " noise " a few millimetres from the head. Telepathic communication could only occur through the medium of an—as yet—unknown type of energy.

It would appear, therefore, that three energy systems act simultaneously within the brain; the chemical energy of the glucose and enzymes which regulate it, the bio-electrical energy recorded by the electroencephalograph, and the PK energy, as it is known.

We might imagine the chemical energy becoming transformed into bio-electrical current and this in turn being transformed into PK energy. We might, for the sake of clarity, divide the functions of the brain into perception and response. By perception we mean that certain of the data continuously streaming in over the senses from the outside are screened out and brought into consciousness, while all the rest are allowed to pass unnoticed; data screened out being presumably of some significance to the individual.

This data may then be sorted into a " rough idea " which is stored in the subconscious mind where it is correlated with all relevant ideas and becomes part of a complex association. Perhaps billions of such associations exist in " storage " in every brain, or at least in every adult brain, ready to be brought into consciousness as keys to action triggered off by appropriate stimuli.

All these processes can be explained in terms of the electrical energy of the brain which has been duplicated in computing machines which, in some cases, achieve better results than the human brain. But the human brain is unique in one respect. It possesses *will*; and *will* can override the logical computations of the intellect and its subconscious and act deliberately in a manner contrary to them.

And so we come to a factor in human behaviour which seems to lend " significance " to a course of action. This feeling of significance, or " rightness " can completely override a person's normal conditioning, the accepted rules of behaviour and even the elementary instincts of self-preservation. We have all experienced acting on a " hunch " or an intuition when the action suggested was contrary to the logic of the situation; hunches and intuition which people throughout the ages and even today believed were manifestations of the devil or angels, depending on the results of the action.

It seems probable, therefore, that will, which might be defined as " the ability of an individual to act in a manner contrary to his conditioning and understanding of a situation, motivated solely by a sense of ' rightness ' " is functional in the psychokinetic field, rather than the bio-electrical processes of the brain.

If this is true, then we might expect that just as there is a continual exchange of ideas going on between people through the printed word, radio, television and so on, there is likewise an interchange, not of ideas, but of " attitudes " between people on another level : that is, on the level of the psychokinetic field.

If this can be assumed, an " idea " might be described as an attitude broken down into verbal and visual symbols. Suppose we witness an incident which arouses our indignation; the indignation is an *attitude* and the words which pour into our minds are an effort to make clear, or to express, our attitude : in short, to communicate our attitude to others. So in telepathic communication, the idea is probably converted by the sender and communicated as such to the recipient who must in turn receive the attitude and convert it back into visual or auditory symbols. If this is the case, it would explain the difficulty of recovering the original message intact, for there are many ways of expressing the same attitude. In fact, it might be said that no two people would express the same attitude in the same manner in exactly the same visual or auditory symbols, except by chance.

Physicians generally recognize the fact that a positive and hopeful mental attitude, if it can be induced in a patient, will increase his chances of recovery, and it has been demonstrated in hundreds of experiments conducted over a period of many years, that such an attitude can easily be produced telepathically and that when this method is used, the incidence of recovery and the speed of recovery are bettered beyond question.

Does the foregoing provide an explanation to the " miracle " cures of Lourdes? At present we cannot say. It could help to explain the basis upon which religions were originally built; the

Fig. 56. Bevatron, one of the world's two most powerful " atom-smashers," which is opening up a new world of atomic physics. At full power, it can accelerate a beam of protons at energies of about 6,200 million electron volts. A super atom-smasher now being built at Brookhaven National Laboratory, Long Island, New York, will produce four times this energy.

United States Information Service.

Fig. 57. This aerial picture of the excavation for the Alternating Gradient Synchrotron at Brookhaven National Laboratory, New York, gives an idea of its size. The world's third most powerful atom-smasher at present in use, the Cosmotron, is housed in the rectangular building in the foreground. The giant machine, expected to be in operation by 1960, may revolutionize our concept of the atomic nucleus.

United States Information Service.

g. 58. *A section of the tunnel, half-a-mile in circumference, which will house America's fantastic new atom-smasher, the Alternating Gradient Synchrotron.*

United States Information Service.

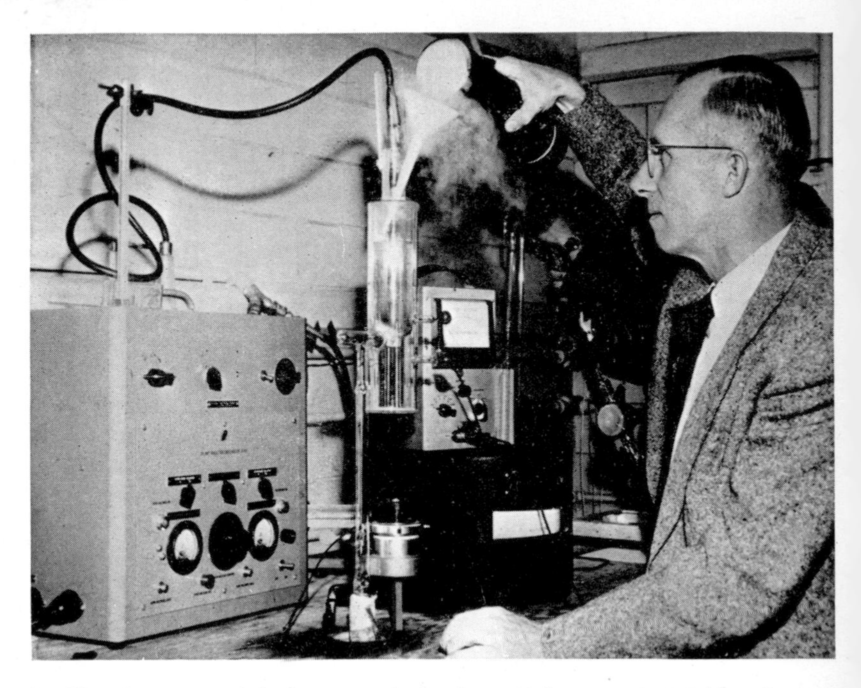

Fig. 59. Preparation of the experiment by Dr. Erwin Müller using the " field-ion " microscope developed by himself.

Fig. 60. Model showing stepped arrangement of the atoms.

First photograph ever taken showing atomic structure of matter.

meaning behind the teachings of Jesus, Buddha and Krishna; the rules that could lead the individual to conscious evolution.

If spiritual communication can be admitted, the idea that creation is a living force that goes on continuously and at various dimensional levels could provide a way of understanding the phenomenon called " death."

Practically all religions offer personal survival as the big reward for a righteous life on earth; it is the fairy-tale promised land where all is peaceful and harmonious, where problems are unknown. Do we stop to think how overwhelmingly boring such an existence would be? Indeed, having served a full life in the physical world, where evolution dominates all things, to be suddenly pitchforked into the promised " haven of rest " would present the human spirit with the prospect of eternal stagnation rather than " eternal life."

What then, is the alternative? By now we are familiar with the idea of the co-existence of various dimensional states; we have observed the Flatlander in his world of shadows and gained a misty impression of a fourth dimension that knows nothing of *Time*. We have seen how these various dimensional " universes " could co-exist without any one of them being discernible to the others although for the sake of illustration it can be shown that one can influence another: a sphere descending on Flatland from three-dimensional space is interpreted as a circle!

Now, if we assume that the post-physical state is, in fact, existence in another dimensional universe, a number of things that have concerned us about this question of survival can be explained. First, the promised " after-life " is not one of idle contentment but one in which evolution plays as vital a part as it has always done in our so-called " physical " universe. It may even be that there is an infinite number of dimensional " universes " to which that part of man which survives physical death is transmitted, according to his degree of conscious evolution. And if evolution is as vital in these other dimensional states as it is in our own, then doubtless there will be more

" deaths " and " rebirths " to follow as the indestructible " spirit " continues on its journey.

How does this hypothesis fit in with our investigations into the paranormal? First of all, we discover that science finds it difficult to come to any conclusion about the truth of so-called spirit communications. The whole thing cannot be tied down and, indeed, it is as elusive as the electron has proved to be in the hands of physicists. Consequently, science has no proof of survival and the whole question remains a matter for personal belief.

Yet one thing may be added. If survival depends upon rebirth into another dimensional universe, can we logically expect " spirit communication " to be anything but what it is? If a sphere descending into a two-dimensional world appears to its inhabitants as a circle that expands and contracts, how can *we* expect communication from another dimension to be anything but intangible and perplexing to us? Were we to project ourselves into a higher dimensional state, as Dunne believed we do in sleep, what kind of impact would we poor three-dimensional creatures have?

Could this account for the " less than intelligent " spirit communications that science has investigated? Within its own dimension, the " spirit " will not be a ghostly will-o'-the-wisp but a being as " real, solid and alive," as we feel ourselves to be real, solid and alive in our three-dimensional universe. But try and make our presence felt in another dimension and that solidity departs, for then we are only part of ourselves.

CHAPTER NINE *The Forbidden Frontier*

> *"We are now approaching a bound beyond which we are forever stopped from pushing our inquiries ... not by the construction of the world, but by the construction of ourselves ... The world fades out and eludes us, because it becomes meaningless."*
>
> PROFESSOR P. W. BRIDGEMAN.

THE UNIVERSE as revealed by twentieth-century science contains more mystery and imagination than any fantasy that could be invented by the mind of man. Perhaps the purposefulness of everything is its most striking attribute. The way the primordial gases become great spiral galaxies, manifest with myriads of stars and, as now seems likely, that out of the same natural processes emerge the planets—the progenitors of life itself. It is hard to believe that all this could be the product of random atomic and chemical activity.

One does not need to peer millions of light years into space, or probe beyond the molecular structure of matter, to discover the purposefulness of life. It is evident in our day-to-day experience. We can marvel at the innate "sense" of protoplasm, which differs little in the lowliest single-celled bacteria from man himself. Starting with a minute fertilized egg no bigger than the full-stop at the end of this sentence, the protoplasm organizes itself to a special form, according to the dictates of the genes carried in the nucleus of every cell, and becomes a beetle, a gazelle or a man.

Consider the words of Dr. Roger Pilkington in the booklet, "How Your Life Began" [1]; he is writing of the factors that govern the development of the human embryo. "Every part of a baby is formed in some wonderful way. The limbs, for example, first appear as little buds without any structure, and then slowly expand and unfold to produce beautifully fashioned

[1] A "Family Doctor" Booklet published by the British Medical Association. Price 1/-

arms and legs. But of all the parts of the human body none has a more curious origin than the eye, with its vast assortment of different types of structure in such a small compass of space. There is the thin and transparent cornea at the front, the coloured cells of the iris, the sensitive cells of the retina or screen at the back which transmit visual impulses to nerve cells for conduction to the brain. And there is, too, the finely fashioned lens itself, as clear as crystal.

" The formation of the eye is a process which shows one of the special methods by which a baby is formed, a method called *induction*. This term means that the presence of one structure actually induces another to arise nearby. In much the same way, the existence of a good sandy beach will eventually induce somebody to build a hotel close by.

" The area of skin which sinks in to form the lens-ball is not laid down definitely in the embryo. The hollow sphere nipped off from the surface of the head begins to fill with a stiff fluid which eventually becomes as transparent as the most optically perfect glass. This is the lens. Finally, the skin overlying the lens becomes clear to form the front surface of the eye, or cornea. The formation of the lens is *induced* by the approach of the optic lobe, and there is every reason to believe that skin from any area of the embryo is perfectly capable of doing the lens trick. Certainly, this is so in animals; even the skin of the belly may be quite able to form a perfect lens. Normally, of course, it never has a chance to do so. It is as though some kind of master plan produces eyes by induction in the place where they are wanted—the front of the head.

" Probably every piece of a baby's body could have become something else, but the planned development results in an orderly body with everything in the right proportions. The reliability of the patterns of inductions and growth, of foldings and heavings, which produce a perfect baby is one of the greatest wonders of life."

Throughout all the processes that go to make up the expanding universe, as much as in man himself, there appears to be as much logic and design as it is possible for mere man to conceive.

Can we be completely satisfied by the biologist's explanation of evolution (p. 45), or must we look beyond the molecular structure of the genes—perhaps right through to the interpenetrating fields of energy that are the true essence of the world of matter? This is not to postulate some analogue of consciousness as being responsible for directing evolution according to some divine master plan, but rather to suggest that, if life *has* purpose, the entire universe may be built upon what, for want of a better term, one might call " a purposive matrix." In this, the evolution of life from inorganic matter while being in a sense " random and experimental " would have an inherent vitality —an upward thrust which is revealed in the tenaciousness of nature. The picture that formed upon this " matrix," however, *would be* experimental—constantly expressing itself in different ways.

Dreams provide an analogy. We may be sitting at a desk writing a letter. We perceive the words flowing from the pen. In the morning, the words in the letter can be recalled to mind. Yet in reality there was neither desk, paper, ink nor words. All were created and sustained by the mental energy of our subconscious mind. And yet, within the temporal dream-world, purposeness had been expressed in words that were not just a meaningless jumble. In this analogy, mental energy is the " purposive matrix " upon which the dream-world has formed; tomorrow, another temporal world may form within the same framework of energy, and we may experience another dream with entirely different situations.

In a similar manner, do the interpenetrating fields of energy revealed by quantum physics serve as a framework for an experimental type of evolution, viable and random, yet relentless in its efforts to produce higher levels of organization? Our whole experience reveals that nature is constantly striving. If evolution is blocked in one direction, it breaks out in another; it is never beaten back.

The inevitable question which has dogged us throughout the last chapter must now be faced: " Is the purposefulness revealed in the universe an attribute of God? "

Within a few decades, science has taken us to the brink of the unknown. It has revealed a universe of unimagined immensity, ablaze with millions of galaxies each containing thousands of millions of stars. There appears to be no thinning out or tangible end to this vast assembly. In the other direction, science has looked beyond the molecular structure of "solid" matter to its atomic essence, and has found nothing more "material" than empty space and fields of energy. Before our eyes the universe is dissolving into a non-material reality. Even the great architect of relativity, Dr. Einstein, who could not have been described by conventional standards as a religious man, found himself humbled by a lifetime of inquiry into the nature of the universe, and discovered at the end of the road a spiritual reality. "My religion," he said,[1] "consists of a humble admiration of the illimitable superior spirit who reveals himself in the slight details we are able to perceive with our frail and feeble minds. That deeply emotional conviction of the presence of a superior reasoning power, which is revealed in the incomprehensible universe, forms my idea of God."

What *is* God? At best, we can only think of an Infinite Consciousness which is beyond our powers of understanding. And though we may apply great ingenuity to our quest, any theories we may have will be unavoidably conditioned by our dimensional limitations.

In fact, speculation of this kind can have no scientific basis. Science makes progress by observing and experimenting, by formulating theories and then ruthlessly testing them. If theory does not agree with fact, it is immediately discarded while those theories which successfully resist the penetrating light of physical inquiry are strengthened and improved. At the present time, for example, astronomers are engaged in making tests of the rival theories of creation—probing the depths of space with giant optical and radio-telescopes for possible irregularities in the make-up of the expanding universe, which must eventually reveal one way or the other whether the universe began at some finite time in the past or is being continually created. In these investigations, scientists are working at the limits of human knowledge; but they do not need to evoke a "God-concept" to prove or disprove a particular theory. The result will be obtained by carefully checking the speeds of recession of the

[1] "The Universe and Dr. Einstein," by Lincoln Barnett. Victor Gollancz Ltd.

remote galaxies and by working out techniques to determine the relative ages of galaxies lying within selected volumes of space.

To inquire into the " purposefulness " of the universe, however, is an altogether different proposition for the answer does not appear to lie within the bounds of the material universe. All the most searching inquiries science has made into the expanding universe and the atom tail off into something that is obscure and intangible, which appears to seal the frontier of three-dimensional creation and effectively bars the way to three-dimensional science.

Here, indeed, is a real psychological problem for, by his nature, man cannot rest content at the forbidden frontier.

The fact that the universe has no apparent end is a difficulty for many people. But how can we define infinity? A dream, perhaps, provides the best analogy, occupying neither space nor time, yet within itself, having all the appearance of an independent world with its own time-scale. Its " inhabitants " move and talk, distances are traversed—yet it has no measurable bounds.

Therefore, just as in sleep we use energy to project a dream, so the universe is a projection of energy in space-time. And yet, from the point of view of some mythical external observer, it occupies neither space nor time; and only to ourselves, buried within the wheeling galaxies, does " solid matter " exist because we, the inhabitants, are fashioned according to the same dynamic laws. In this sense, we are dream characters. So, rather than thinking of the universe as great systems of wheeling matter, we ought to regard it in the same light as, let us say, a thought or a dream.

So the universe is " real " in the sense that a dream is real. And it is as futile to seek its confines as it is to seek the confines of a dream.

In this respect, the universe (or an electron) has no more reality to the scientist than a concept of God. By the same token, the *reason* for creation is equally obscure. Can we even count on reason having any significance outside our own dimension? The idea that, despite our proud aspirations, we may have no special meaning in the scheme of things, is repugnant to us—and indeed, if we have not, the foundation of human ethics must fall.

Thus, any inquiry into the " mechanics " of creation and the reason and purpose behind it, will have no greater meaning than, let us say, a party charade. Just as the physicist can interpret the *effects* of an electron but cannot analyse it and say precisely what it is, so we can only interpret the *effects* of creation; we cannot investigate the Creator. It is no more perplexing than that the eye should experience the sensation of colour, which we call red, though the question: " Why *is* red? " is meaningless.

Having made this point—and for the benefit of those people who, like the authors, enjoy such things—let us attempt to construct a charade which seeks to account for creation. With a little ingenuity, charades of this kind can be made to fit any theory. It is rather like working out a problem in mathematics if you begin with the answer and work backwards; only in this case, one finds the problem posed in obscure and incomprehensible symbols.

We might begin with an Infinite Consciousness.

We cannot begin to analyse such a condition, only to record the fact that something with these attributes must exist (if that term is valid) without contrast or comparison. It is a state of rest. We might call it " *the Dormant Mind*." In this state, there is neither reason nor unreason, harmony or discord, good or evil; such things can only be experienced by comparison, and this faculty is obviously lacking in a state of being which is unique and absolute. In order to realize itself—to *progress*—the All-embracing Consciousness must assume creative powers. It must create from within itself another complex. But what can be created which will permit growth and evolution of the Whole? It is no use the Whole creating facets of itself—for these would be mere puppets which would dance but only at the call of the Master. What is required is something that, while remaining *part* of the Whole, *will be capable of independent growth and expression,* for only in this way can the Whole secure its own evolution. This might be called " *The Awakening*." Herein the " material universe " is cast, and yet not rigidly in form as a sculptor would create his masterpiece, but in the subtle interplay of vibrant energies—the building together of atoms. It is much more a creation of *thought* than of *structure*, like thought-waves rippling towards an idea. There is no cataclysmic explosion that brings the universe into being in one searing instant but the subtle emergence of vibrant energies; " and with the thought," space and time come into existence.

Charade or not, this explanation is unlikely to satisfy the cynic. " If this monomorphic God is responsible for creation," he will say, " then what created *Him*? Surely, something has got to be at work before something else can be created!"

Here, once again, we are confronted with the question of time. Yet time, as we have seen, enters the picture only when we limit our interpretation of things; beyond the narrow confines of our physical world, it has no meaning.

To our petty minds, it seems logical to assume that " something must exist before something else can be created," but we forget that this argument holds only when we think in three-dimensional terms. How could we interpret a five-dimensional existence? It is no use trying to add another two walls to our three-dimensional room. We have to abandon all our existing concepts, for a five-dimensional universe would have laws of its own which to us would be quite incomprehensible. How then could we hope to understand the workings of an *Infinite* Consciousness? It is like the nuclear physicist and his studies of the atom. He may feel certain that something which he calls an electron exists but his three-dimensional instruments can only interpret its effects. Similarly, to demand proof of Ultimate Reality, God, or whatever else you choose to call it, is merely to acknowledge one's own ignorance, and to attempt any discussion of origins in three-dimensional terms can only lead to frustration. We must seek a more subtle link!

Let us return to the dream analogy. When we dream, we do not create actual three-dimensional people yet, within our subconscious, these characters live and move. Our three-dimensional universe, which to us seems so " solid " and tangible may be like that; we may think of matter and energy as finite disturbances in an infinite consciousness outside the time factor of the physical world! And it might be that, like space and time, matter and energy are purely manifestations in the limited consciousness. Indeed, on this basis, we may imagine the co-existence of many universes of three, four, five and more dimensions.

If this idea is difficult to grasp, it may help to recall again that the various radiations with which we are familiar on the earth differ dimensionally: X-rays, wireless waves and light waves are distinguished by their own peculiar wave-lengths and to detect them we must use different instruments. The human eye, tuned to a small wave-band in the visible spectrum, is totally blind to all other kinds of radiation. If it were tuned to another wave-length, say X-rays, we could never see the stars. And it may be the same with the three-dimensional universe to which our consciousness is tuned; we could be perfectly blind to other dimensional states which may represent higher or lower stages in the evolutionary scale. And because the " Consciousness " behind it all is not limited to the " logic " of a three-dimensional world, the question of origins can never be answered in these homely three-dimensional terms. Indeed, we must consider ourselves as manifestations in the limited consciousness just as our dreams are limited manifestations of our own subconscious. Within the limited consciousness of our universe, it is logical to expect one thing to lead to another, but where " Ultimate Reality " is concerned the idea is probably no more than the shadow of our own ignorance.

CHAPTER TEN *In Search of God*

" If God did not exist, it would be necessary to invent him."

VOLTAIRE.
Poem to the author of " Les trois imposteurs," 1769.

DESPITE THE fact that science is unable to prove the existence of God, religion plays an important part in every society, whether primitive or highly developed, and from the very beginning, man has instinctively sought consolation and security in some higher power than himself.

Primitive man worshipped the sun, the moon and the stars. He interpreted the lightning flash as the wrath of the gods, and in the warmth of the sun he found comfort in the belief that the gods were pleased. In time of adversity he fell to the ground; he begged for sunshine or for rain—or for victory over his enemies. Everything he could not explain for himself he attributed to the work of the gods. And always he sought to win their favour. He was their slave and to appease them he made offerings and sacrifices.

In the course of time, as man became increasingly aware of the world in which he lived, his outlook slowly changed. Astronomy taught him that it was unnecessary to attribute to his primitive gods the motions of the heavenly bodies; Darwin brought a new understanding of how life began which rejected the idea of a " special creation "; while modern biology left no doubt that disease and pestilence were not evidence of God's wrath but merely the by-products of evolution.

In view of all that man has discovered it may seem incredible that many Christian people still regard everything the Bible has to say as literal truth from which nothing can be subtracted. To them, the story of Adam and Eve is more credible than evolution; the Flood and God's despairing of mankind is more acceptable than the quality of mercy, and passive adherence to the written word is superior to the freedom of thought and experience. In fact, the Bible is so full of contradiction, particularly regarding the nature of God, that it is difficult to understand how anyone can still regard it as an infallible document.

We argue over words and phrases as though they had been transcribed from tape-recordings, forgetting that they represent ideas and statements which have been handed down from generation to generation and variously interpreted by peoples of widely differing understanding. Adam and Eve were probably the invention of a "prophet" who sought to point a moral, and the Flood, a natural (and quite localized) disaster.[1] Modified over the centuries, the useful working first principles of early sages became touchstones of orthodoxy, cornerstones of dogma and cobblestones of persecution: the building materials of religions and the die in which primitive man's conception of God was cast. And because punishment was something that could be readily understood, the same human frailty was attributed to the Creator; the Flood became a punishment for man's misdeeds—and God something, or someone, to fear!

To some people, God is the formless, Infinite Mind, that gives meaning and purpose to all creation. Others who take the literal view, that "man was created in the image of God," think of Him as a kind of superior human being of infinite goodness. Indeed, many people appear to retain their childhood impression of God as a benevolent old gentleman, a kind of saintly Father Christmas, abiding somewhere beyond the clouds. One is reminded of the caterpillar and the beetle who met in the underbrush of a forest glade. Philosophically, the caterpillar lifts his head and gazes around at the tall grass that seemingly stretches away for ever on all sides of the toadstool which shelters them. "What a BIG caterpillar it must have been who created all this!" he muses, oblivious of his companion's growing indignation: "What a brain; what an intellect!" "A caterpillar indeed!" retorts his companion. "I'll have you

[1] "The Bible as History," Hodder and Stoughton, 1956. According to Dr. Werner Keller, the Biblical Flood occurred about 4000 B.C. affecting an area north-west of the Persian Gulf, roughly 400 miles long and 100 miles wide, centred on the Rivers Tigris and Euphrates.

know the Creator was a GIANT and quite superior beetle!" They went their separate ways and, it is said, never spoke again.

However we picture God, it is evident that man's conception of him has changed a great deal over the centuries. The God of the Old Testament is a tribal god who reflects little more than man's own intolerance.

Man looked upon God as a means to his own ends with the result that he has created an image which is little more than the reflection of his own selfish desires. If God is all the things man believes him to be, he is but a pale shadow of what man himself has achieved in a few Ages of groping awareness. Is it surprising, therefore, that the God of orthodox Christianity comes out as something less than the living example of a man like Albert Schweitzer?

The evidence for evolution is now so immense that it cannot be seriously disputed. Yet, because evolution does not actually take place before our eyes, there are still people who cling to the idea of a Special Creation, believing that any other view must be in opposition to established religious principles. It is true that if we take a literal interpretation of Genesis, with its reference to the six days of creation and the story of Adam and Eve, natural history and religion do not exactly go hand in hand. But then, must everything we find in the Bible be accepted exactly as it is written?

It has long been argued that the Bible is subject to interpretation in different ways, that important truths contained therein have been expressed symbolically. It is also nothing new to say that many features of the Bible (especially the Old Testament) reflect the same limitations we have been discussing with regard to man himself, that others have been misinterpreted, while still others have suffered through mistranslation. Indeed, in view of the antiquity of the manuscripts it would be remarkable if these things had not occurred.

Again, anyone who has attempted to translate another language into English will acknowledge the difficulty of matching words so perfectly that they mean exactly what the foreign author intended. Often, a direct equivalent of a word does not exist and another has to be found which possesses nearly—but not precisely—the original meaning. Might this not be the explanation of an otherwise reasonable statement on evolution set out in Genesis in which the word " day " actually means " period "—a period of time?

With the coming of Jesus Christ, a new concept of God emerged which turned fear into love, and punishment into compassion. But like the concepts of all the great spiritual geniuses who believed passionately in human freedom, the brotherhood of man and the supremacy of love, the teachings of Jesus fell victim to transcription, and the intellectual clarity and consistency which their chroniclers sought, to the foundation of rigid doctrines which split mankind and revived the fear of God.

How does Jesus fit into the picture? It is the teaching of the Christian Church that he was a unique creation—the personification of God on earth—" the Son of God."

But what if Jesus was not?

If we are intent on Truth and not merely seeking to defend established dogma, it is a question that should, at least, be considered. In fact, the virgin birth of Jesus is one of the most primitive ideas of the Christian Faith. It was a common belief among the people of his time that a Messiah could only be born of a virgin, and long before Jesus appeared man was according his gods this virtue.

Could Jesus Christ, Gautama Buddha and other great world teachers have emerged in the normal course of evolution?

It is the transmission of genes from generation to generation that determines the characteristics a certain individual will have. It does not follow that because father or mother is gifted in a certain direction that the son or daughter will necessarily inherit the same gift. In the next generation, the " gene combination " that produced a brilliant artist will be rearranged by the infusion of other gene characteristics that, more likely than not, will result in a new individual with only average aspirations. There are, of course, notable exceptions—the Bach family, for example.

Thus, we have in the world a vast reservoir of genes which

with each new generation is shuffled, like a pack of cards, to produce new combinations, some of which may have great hereditary potentialities, which may be revealed in great artists and musicians, or equally in great humanitarians. But with the credit side of life's balance sheet, we must also accept the debit side, which is the price we pay for all the beauty and greatness that man has been able to give to the world. Yet it would be an unjust god who pitchforked the debtors into the acrid flames of Hell.

Clearly then, the idea of a god who rewards good and punishes evil is primitive. For one thing, it assumes that all men enter this world with equal potentialities, whereas we know that the particular gene-combination a man inherits may greatly influence his life. Consequently, a homosexual, or even a murderer, may be guilty in the eyes of society but he can scarcely be guilty in the eyes of a just god.

There are men in our prisons and institutions today against whom the scales were heavily tilted before they were born. There are others, representing the highest and best of our stock, who are highly respected for their extreme self-denial and service to humanity. And, of course, there are many shades and variations of people in between. To a degree, we cannot help what we are; and we have little choice but to express ourselves according to the imprint of the particular gene-combination we inherit.

This does not, of course, mean that one man is predestined to become a saint and another a sinner, but it does mean that certain tendencies in these directions may be present as a human characteristic. If this should seem unjust, it is only because of the peculiar ideas we have about ourselves in relation to the universe. It is a law of nature that experiment plays a fundamental part in the life-building process. Were it not so, there would be no great heights for man to climb and conversely no great depths for him to fall. It would be a steady-state existence with neither greatness nor decadence.

Thus we might regard the outcome of highly gifted people in the same light as, let us say, the possibility of making a winning forecast in a football pool. To win the big dividend, one has to select a certain combination from millions of possible combinations, just as in evolution we have enormous numbers of gene combinations being thrown together from generation to generation which produce individuals of varying degrees of attainment. Few of us enjoy the supreme gift of a da Vinci, a Beethoven or a Shakespeare. To evolve these highly gifted people, nature spawns in millions. One might say that generations of average plants have to live and die in obscurity to produce a single flower of incredible beauty that blooms for one summer. Is it really any more fantastic, then, to think of Jesus and other great figures of religious history as the products of natural processes.

To many people, the idea of Jesus as a man will be repugnant, not merely because of the instilled conditioning that " the Faith " entails, but because of the many wonderful things that are attributed to him. That Jesus was a most remarkable personality cannot be doubted, but only now are we becoming aware of powers that lie behind the threshold of the senses available to mortal man.

Mystical experiences, for example, are not limited to Jesus alone; they have been experienced by the " masters " of all religions—by poets, artists, mystics and saints, of all races and creeds and by numbers of ordinary people as well. Only today are we beginning to examine the powers of faith healing—the " laying on of hands." Although the medical world is sceptical, remarkable things appear to have been achieved; and certainly, the attested healings at Lourdes [1] must rank high on the list of present-day miracles. Again, we must not fall into the trap of believing that all so-called " miracles " are associated with the Christian Faith. The literature of the East is full of stories of miracles, and indeed there are today in the austere practices of the Yogas of India and Tibet examples of happenings which appear to rank with some of the traditional miracles.

All this is not to deny that the world has known—and, for that matter, is still experiencing—remarkable things which, at present, are beyond the sphere of logic or scientific understanding. In probing the mysteries of the paranormal, we are today in rather the position of early men who saw in the lightning

[1] " The Mystery of Lourdes," by Ruth Cranston. Evans Brothers, London.

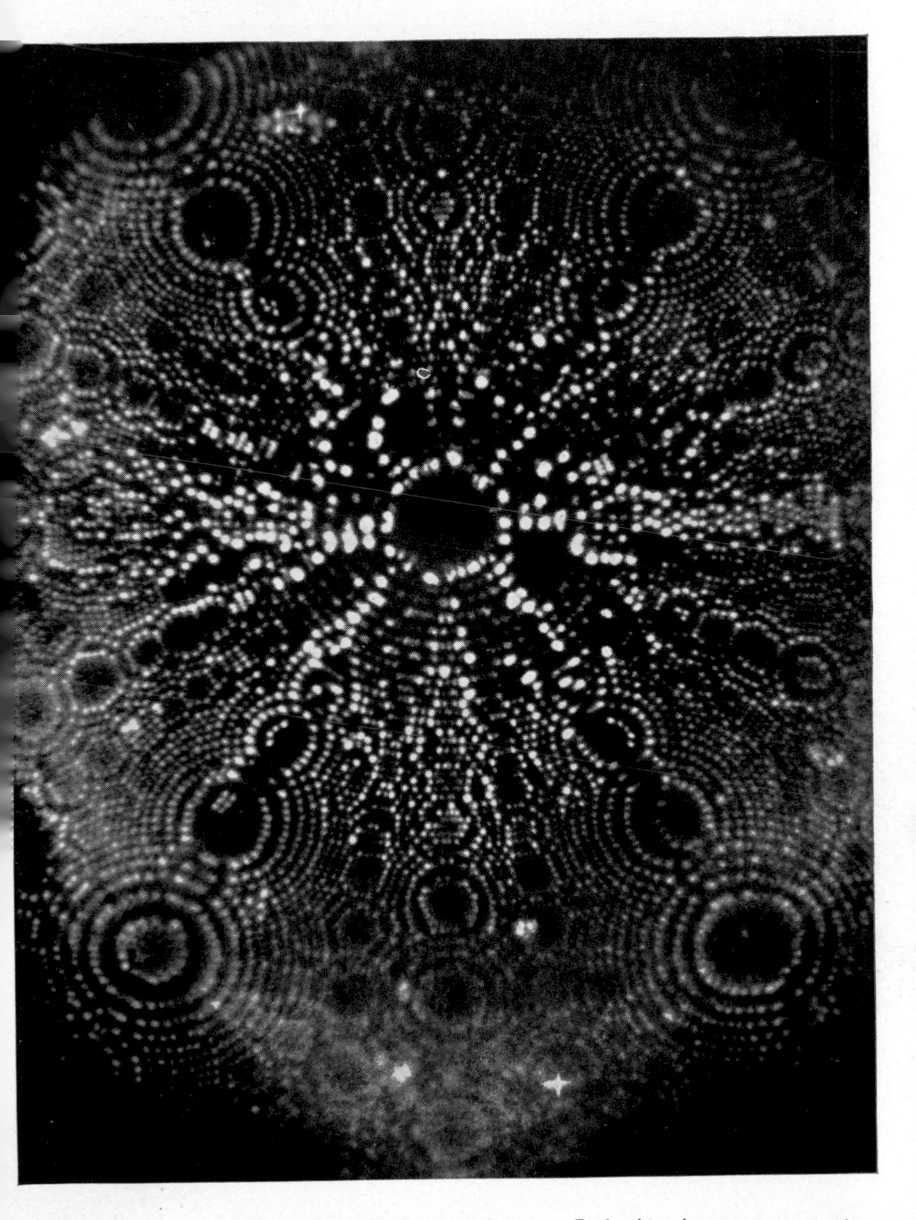

Fig. 61. Tip of a tungsten wire magnified 2,750,000 times. Each white dot represents an atom of tungsten, revealing that the atomic structure consists of planes (the dark areas) lying one above the other in the form of a step pyramid. So clear is the reproduction obtained with the " field-ion " microscope that another photograph of the same wire taken the following day will show the number of atoms which have changed position overnight.

First photograph ever taken showing atomic structure.

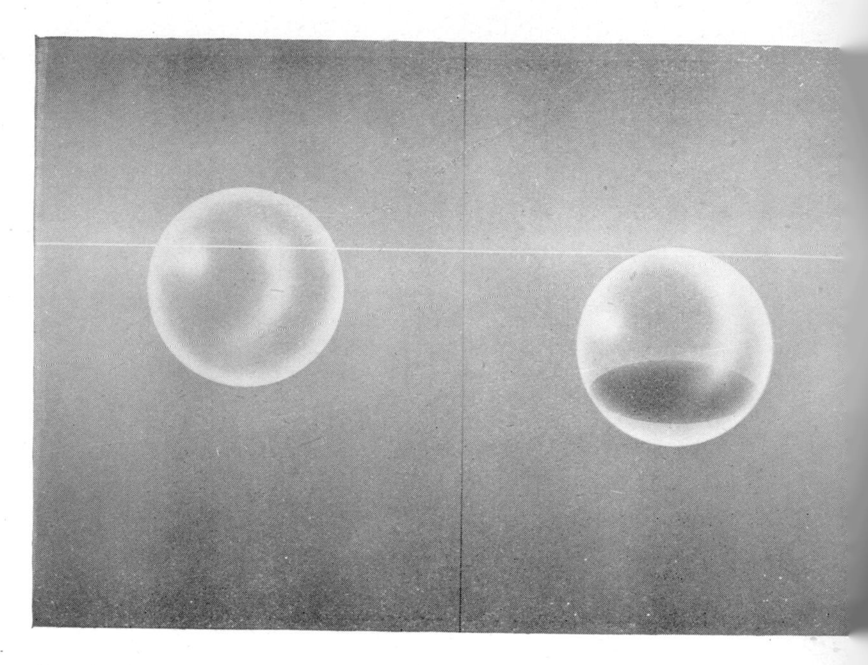

Fig. 62. A sphere descends upon the mythical world of Flatland. Having no conception as a circle. As the sphere cuts the plane of Flatland, the circle grows from a point until hal it vanishes altogether. How will the Flatlander, whose outlook is limited to two dimensions (le the external observer in t

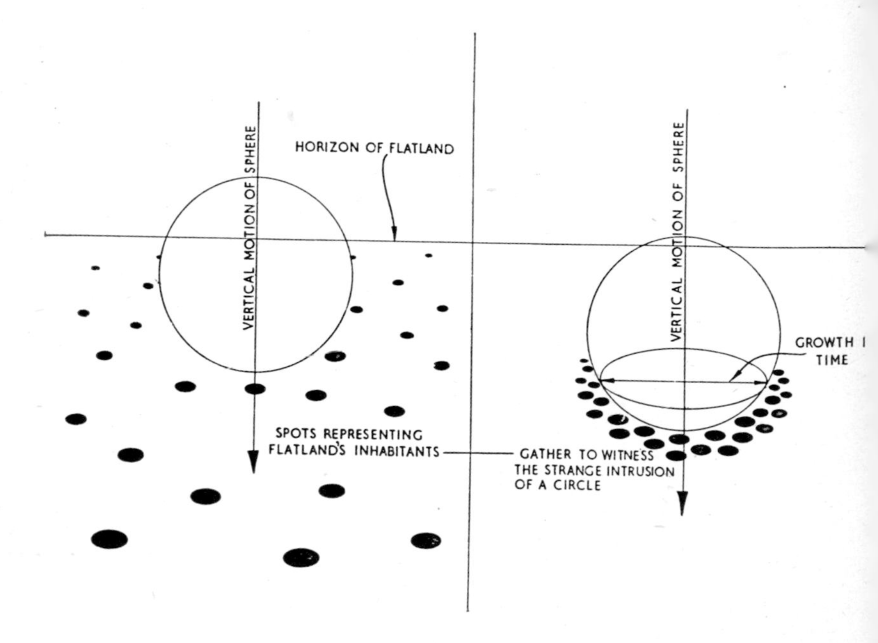

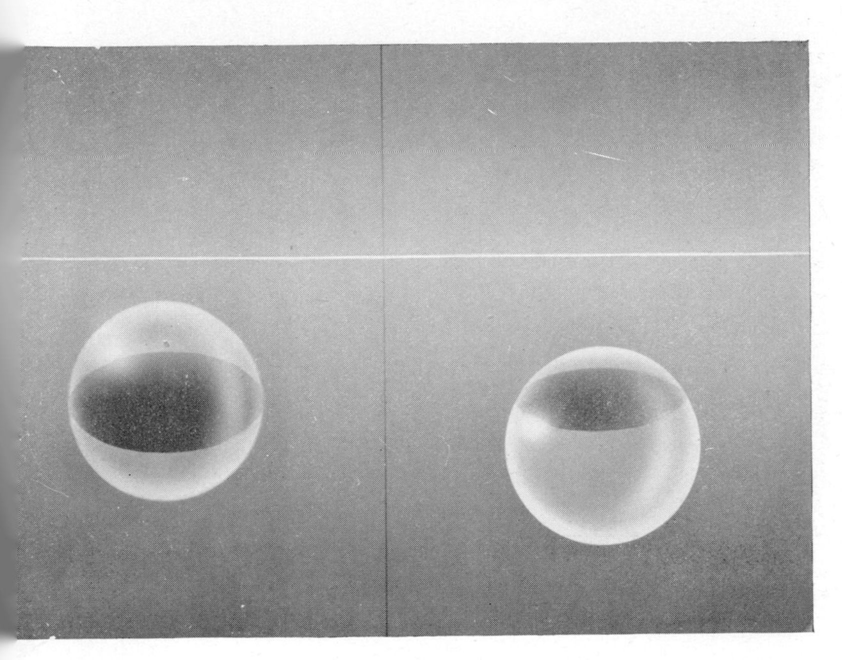

l dimension (and hence of solidity), the shadow-like inhabitants will interpret the intruder has passed through; the circle then begins to contract until, finally, as the sphere departs, eadth) regard this phenomenon? He will mistakenly attribute to GROWTH IN TIME what ;ons regards as solidity and motion.

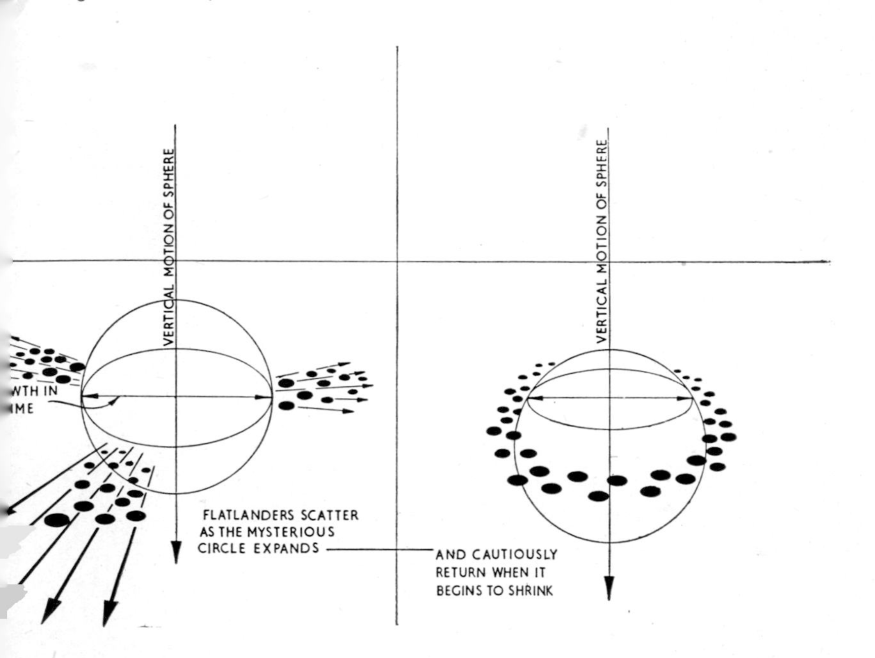

Fig. 63. The prototype of the H-bomb was exploded in the Pacific on November 1, 1952, when coral island half-a-mile long and a quarter-of-a-mile wide was scourged from the earth in a fracti of a second. The nuclear fire-ball, hot as the surface of the sun, expanded to a diameter of thre and-a-quarter miles and was estimated to be big enough to destroy the heart of New York and k half the population of Long Island.

Fig. 64. A giant radio-active dust cloud mushroomed out until it hung like a canopy over 100 miles wide, extending fully 25 miles into the atmosphere.

The threat to mankind by man's own hand.

United States Atomic Energy Commission.

flash evidence of God's wrath. We simply have no explanation that does not involve conjuring up the direct intervention of God or, on the other hand, of concealing our ignorance with scepticism. And yet, in speaking of miracles, what can rank with the great cosmic miracle of life itself—the fashioning, through evolution, of mind and personality out of neutral impersonal stuff—the drifting dust clouds of galactic space?

It is no use complaining that, by disposing with the "supernatural," we are disposing of the Creator. What do we mean by "supernatural" anyway? The dictionary defines it as "that which is above, or beyond, the laws of nature." But this does not mean that many of the things we do not understand will not one day become apparent to us. Under the penetrating eye of the scientist, our conception of nature—the universe—changes from generation to generation, so that what was "supernatural" yesterday is entirely "natural" today.

In less enlightened times, there were people who considered it a heresy to pry into the secrets of the universe, believing that man should confine himself to the world into which he was born. If scientific inquiry continues this search, they said, everything will be rendered commonplace and there will be nothing left at which to marvel. Such outlooks stem from a fear that science is demolishing, brick by brick, the foundation of religion, whereas in fact, nothing could be further from the truth. Each new scientific discovery has revealed a greater mystery, so that today the scientist stands amazed at his discoveries—on the one hand, the macrocosm, the great expanding universe with its millions upon millions of stellar systems, and on the other, the microcosm—the fantastic realm of the atom where matter shrinks from reach and vibrant energies replace all that is "solid and tangible."

To reveal something which was once unknown, and hence "supernatural," is therefore not to render it any less significant in the pattern of creation—a stone holds within it a mystery as great as does the universe.

Why, then, should there be any difficulty between the revelations of science and the postulates of religion? Why should it be more acceptable that God should create man, as a conjuror produces a rabbit out of a hat, *by interfering with the natural laws of his own creation*? Is it any less credible that he should emerge from natural processes already at work in the universe or any less wonderful that " intelligence " should have emerged from shapeless clouds of gas? Does the latter hypotheses suggest a less *purposive* creation or that infinite design does not prevail in the universe?

Out of those " background materials," now identified as hydrogen gas, has come not only the great island galaxies that populate the expanding universe but a whole cavalcade of evolution—living beings, with thoughts, ideas and feelings, able to create for themselves instruments with which to extend their grasp of nature, and to express themselves in great works of art.

Evolution has not merely produced order out of disorder—it has produced personality out of neutral, impersonal stuff. This upward building process is as much responsible for the mind, the personality, and the spirit of man as it is for inert matter. What other conclusion can we draw than that we are in the midst of a creative evolution, and that the universe is a living complex of immense potentiality?

CHAPTER ELEVEN *The Last Freedom*

The devil and a friend of his were walking along the street, when, some distance away, they saw a man stoop down, pick something up and put it in his pocket. The friend said to the devil, " What did that man pick up? " " He picked up a piece of Truth," said the devil. " That is a bad business for you, then," said the friend. " Oh, not at all," the devil replied. " I am going to let him organise it."

CARLO SUARES,
Krishnamurti (1933).

RELIGION HAS been called a psychological necessity. Freud and others have tended to regard all religions as being founded on illusion and their study as nothing more than a branch of anthropology and psychology. At the other extreme, there are vast millions of ordinary people who see in a particular religion an end in itself and are happy to surrender to its every demand. Such religions have been responsible for the sheep-like attachment of millions of people whose demands will never rise above the comfort and security afforded by their belief in some traditionalized doctrine.

Most people living in the Western World profess Christianity and the great majority will never come into contact with any other religion. Yet had these same people been born in the Eastern hemisphere, local custom and tradition would have decided quite differently about their affiliations and just as unconsciously they would have been absorbed into one of the religions of the East. But each of these, whether it is Christianity, Hinduism, Mohammedanism, or any other, will be regarded by its followers as the " one true way! " The result is that the world's religions, instead of making for the brotherhood of men, are continually widening the gulf of understanding.

Religion, as the dictionary defines it, is " The recognition of God as an object of love and obedience "; is it belonging to a religious sect, repeating prayer, or reading the sacred books?

Orthodox religion is all these things. It reveres, it idolizes—and it expounds dogma. But if purpose exists in the universe, can one really imagine that man's entire function is to acknowledge his Creator passively as an act of faith? Does it not also imply a search for Truth at all levels of human consciousness? Indeed, by indulging in traditional stereotyped prayers, without understanding, we are carrying out a routine that must inevitably destroy our powers of thought and reasoning. The mind, which stands at the head of evolution, instead of being used creatively, is dulled and restricted.

We may no longer countenance slavery of the body, but slavery of the mind is something we still accept without question. There are many examples throughout the strata of the world's religions, but the ruthlessness with which this process is pursued is nowhere more forcefully expressed than in the Catholic "Law on Marriage." Consider, for example, this statement: "A 'mixed marriage' (a marriage between a Catholic and one who, though baptised, does not profess the Catholic Faith) is strictly forbidden, nor will the Church even tolerate it unless in a special case there be a grave reason and the following conditions be fulfilled: That *all* the children who may be born of the marriage shall be baptized, and brought up, in the Catholic Faith . . ."

Thus, the child of a "mixed marriage" is destined, before birth, to view the universe through a special pair of "spectacles" and will be indoctrinated into the particular "Laws of God" which support the idea of man's unique creation in Adam and Eve, the virgin birth of Jesus, and the infallibility of the Pope. How restrictive, in the face of all that man has learned of the universe—and in view of all that lies beyond his present range of vision—to believe that the mystery of life can be wrapped up and dogmatized so neatly! How can one religious system, or any religion, for that matter—and there are many throughout the world—presume to destroy so completely the creative powers inherent in a human life *before that life has even begun*? Indeed, there is still slavery in the world, in a more subtle form perhaps than the harnessing of bodily labour, but nevertheless one which is exceedingly wearing to the human spirit. One may recall that it was not so long ago in history that witches and scientific reformers were burnt in the name of religion. Who can doubt that future generations will regard the present attitude to innocent life as less inhuman? Indeed, the folly of dogmatizing anything—whether in the field of science or religion—is highly dangerous if we are seeking truth and not merely striving to defend established ideas.

There is today in the hearts of people everywhere a crying need to believe in something that is assured and permanent. The fact that man sees around him evidence of impermanence and the law of survival of the fittest, does not deter him. His pride is enormous and he desperately needs to be assured that he will survive this world of uncertainty and despair.

To this end, credulity is stretched to the limit and he is willing to believe in anything that appears to hold the vital promise of security. He is willing to accept anything that serves as a foothold, despite all reason, and is content to replace thought with a blind unreasoning faith. Hence the success of fundamentalists like Dr. Billy Graham whose " Hell-fire " teachings (ironically, in the name of Jesus) put fear in place of love. " Unless we make a declaration for Christ, we are lost," Graham says, " . . . there is no time to reason what it all means; there is need only for faith." In other words, we are asked to come before God as servile beings without spirit—contributing nothing.

In the Christian World, there are many people who look down upon the Hindu and his idols; and yet for all who make idols with their hands, there are millions who apply the same negative attitude in the creation of mental images, around which the mind stagnates amid the relentless dogmas and rituals of organized religion. Indeed, numbers of people who are essentially rational and clear thinking in their working hours, not excluding some scientists, come to religious problems as though they scarcely possessed a mind at all!

Often, a Christian is shocked to learn that there are millions of deeply religious people who have never heard of the Jewish Carpenter. Yet Dr. Billy Graham says that only through Jesus

Christ can we be assured of the Kingdom of Heaven. One might inquire about the fate of the peoples of India and China. Are they to be victimized because, by accident of birth, they happen to live in places where the name of Jesus of Nazareth is unknown? Are these peoples to be denied " eternal life " simply because they were born " on the wrong side of the tracks? "

There are so many questions one would like to ask. How far do we go back in history for man to qualify for life eternal? What happened more than 2,000 years ago before Jesus appeared? Was there no Heaven then?

Convention considers man as though he had always been as he is today. But, in fact, the age of man has scarcely begun. Jeans gave a striking analogy in his book, " The Universe Around Us." " Take a penny; on the penny place a postage stamp and put both on the top of Cleopatra's Needle. The age of the earth is represented by the 70-foot column, the entire period of man's existence by the coin, and the length in which he has been slightly civilised by the stamp. A column of stamps thousands of feet, perhaps a mile, high would indicate the period during which life should be possible on earth."

In another million years—indeed if he survives his childhood —man will not be as he is now. But the " fundamentalists " do not take into account the presence in our midst of the vital life-force called evolution. To them, man was literally fashioned by the hand of God—and to believe otherwise is tantamount to heresy.

Indeed, one might inquire what special achievement singles man out as fit to continue his life in a spiritual heaven. At what stage is it assumed that he breaks away from the " lesser " animals? Do they also survive? And if man alone enjoys this distinction, do his remote ancestors of the forest also survive? Where do we draw the line?

Although it is true that religion was the cradle from which culture and civilization have sprung, it is equally true that the religions which have *emerged from civilization* have tended to divide mankind. And yet, it is remarkable how similar these religions are in their essence, each being centred in a belief in a god or gods, and invariably there is a prophet or "enlightened one"—often the founder of the religion itself—who is worshipped also. In many religions, the latter is regarded as an incarnation of "God in the flesh"; for example, "Jesus, the Son of God," born of a virgin. Similarly, according to Buddhist doctrine, Guatama Buddha was one of twenty-four divine incarnations of the Great Buddha, while Hinduism has a number of gods who, for a time, are said to have taken the form of mortals. Vishnu, for example, is supposed to have incarnated several times, not only as a man but in sub-human guise, as fish, tortoise, boar and man-lion.

It is surprising, too, how often the idea of virgin birth crops up in the history of the religions. In China, Lao-tze, the traditional founder of Taoism, is supposed to have been carried in his mother's womb for seventy-two years before being born into the world infinitely wise. Similarly, Mahavira, who founded Jainism in India, is believed to have been placed in his mother's womb in a miraculous manner. In Persia, Zoroaster is supposed to have been miraculously conceived after his 15-years-old mother had experienced fourteen prophetic visions foretelling the birth of a Divine Son.

Nowhere is this similarity more apparent than in the lives, as traditionally recorded, of Jesus Christ and Guatama Buddha. Guatama's mother was a virgin for thirty-two months; her son performed thirty-two healing miracles, was transfigured, fed 500 people with one small cake, had a disciple who walked on the water; and when he was taken to a temple for a ceremony, conformed but said it was unnecessary.

Explaining this in his interesting book, "Comparative Religions,"[1] Dr. A. C. Bouquet says: "The whole question of the transmission of the sacred literature of India is a very unsettled one. . . . What must be honestly reckoned with is the probable existence of a large number of appropriate folk-tales about holy persons, which influenced alike the traditions about Jesus and Guatama, and led them to assume certain forms."

Whatever truth lies behind the stories which have come down to us about the miracles associated with the great figures of religious history, nothing surprises us more than the parallels

[1] Pelican Books (A.89), third and revised edition, 1950, p. 158.

which exist in the basic philosophies of the world's religions. Consider the following:

Buddhism : " Hurt not others with that which pains yourself." (From the Udanavarga 5.18.)

Christianity : " All things whatsoever ye would that man should do to you, do ye even so to them; for this is the law of the prophets." (From the Bible, St. Matthew 7.12.)

Hinduism : " Do naught to others which if done to thee would cause thee pain." (From the Mahabharata 5.1517.)

Judaism : " What is hurtful to yourself do not to your fellow man." (Talmud.)

Taoism : " Regard your neighbour's gain as your own gain: and regard your neighbour's loss as your own loss." (T'ai Shang Kan Ying P'ien.)

There are literally hundreds of other examples which appear to reveal a common background of intuitive experience, shared by Christian saints equally as by eastern mystics; and in another sense, there is the deeply religious conviction that all searchers after truth have found, saint, mystic and scientist alike, of an underlying reality to the physical world.

In view of the discoveries in quantum physics, there is a growing belief that science is coming out in support of religious principles. The destruction of nineteenth century belief in a mechanical concept of the universe and the substitution of a universe of energy, almost one might say, of thought, is one example of the way science has progressed in this direction. It is true that this concept of a non-material reality has deep spiritual significance, though it is one in which there need be no rejoicing on the part of the formalized religions.

A broader understanding of the universe and the part that evolution plays in it must, in fact, ultimately lead to a revolution in religious teaching if Christianity and other formalized religions are to survive. Indeed, it is not unlikely that the advance of knowledge over the next hundred years will bring about a marked decline in dogmatic belief. This is not to suggest that the great principles established by Jesus and others will be overthrown. Such truths are eternal and belong to all humanity but before man can be set free, *the God created in man's image* must be discarded, together with the rigid dogmas that have grown up and deprived the living truth of Jesus and other inspired teachers of their impact and meaning. Christianity, at its most dogmatic, is unsatisfying to thinking people and cannot long survive. Thus, although church-leaders may find new heart in the non-material reality revealed by modern physics, this will have little relevance to religion as it is formally organized.

The psychologist would say that if people find hope and security in some particular doctrine, however illogical it may seem, it does no particular harm. If dogmatic belief provides stability in adversity, when everything in life seems dark and insecure, it is something to hold on to—a kind of " spiritual crutch "—and serves a useful purpose.

And yet, if man is to enter the reality of religious experience, this crutch must be discarded. The path of religious exploration is not necessarily the way of all men, however; for it is no easy journey! It means giving up the security of religions which have everything conveniently sorted out and labelled and which demand nothing but blind, unreasoning faith.

We cannot possibly improve upon the words of Raynor C. Johnson, in his book, " The Imprisoned Splendour." " The large majority of people," he says, " are as yet insufficiently developed on the buddhic [1] level to be capable of a sustained voyage of spiritual discovery—of that effort of self-discipline and meditation capable of yielding indubitable insights and knowledge. For these, an organized framework of religious belief having symbolic expressions on a still lower level of significance, as in ritual and ceremonial, may be the most appropriate and satisfactory expression of religious feeling. To deplore this is to quarrel with the time-process. We do not complain that a baboon has no appreciation of beauty, that primitive man has left us no legacy of mathematics or music, or that Central African tribes are not conversant with the finer shades of courtesy or self-sacrifice. The limitations and the tragedy of the

[1] Buddhic—coming from a Sanskrit word meaning " wisdom."

contending religious systems of belief may be the growing pains of humanity on its spiritual pilgrimage."

Dogmatic belief is scarcely in keeping with our experience. In the slight details we have been able to perceive, we have found that we are the inhabitants of a Cosmos which is vigorous, creative, and constantly seeking new ways of expression.

Can man be any less creative?

Does life in the incredible universe mean no more to man than a continual round of pleasure, entertainment and spiritual sedatives?

The way of religious exploration is not the path of science although it has something of the pure scientist's approach. We have seen that science has long ceased to be dogmatic over its discoveries, regarding each new finding merely as a stepping-stone to further knowledge. In following this practice, the astronomers and physicists of the twentieth century have become modest indeed.

In setting out on some particular inquiry, the scientist must be entirely detached, constantly probing and testing, yet never allowing his mind to crystallize around any theory. Even when, at length, he has arrived at a conclusion, he must be honest enough to admit that further probing, perhaps with finer instruments, will eventually lead to deeper and more difficult problems, just as one man may look at a stone and define it as "solid and quite inert" while another, with more specialized knowledge, will see the same stone abounding with energy yet comprising mostly empty space.

The true scientist, though he may have all kinds of prejudices and inhibitions in matters outside his profession, must be scrupulously impartial in his search for scientific truth. Why should this essential freedom be denied us in our religious inquiries?

The seemingly large expanse which is the surface of this planet gives us the illusion that we are important inhabitants of a huge realm. We have tremendous pride and self-esteem, and among our people are the writers of many books with such resounding titles as: "The Nature of the Universe," "The Meaning of Life," "Mind and Reality" and so on; to look after our destiny, we have even evoked the protection of tribal gods. Not only have we divisions of religions and ideologies but we have seen fit to maintain national and racial barriers.

And yet, in relation to the greater universe, our " huge realm " is nothing but a speck of dust trapped in a sunbeam.

CHAPTER TWELVE *The End—or the Beginning?*

> *"It will ever remain incomprehensible that our generation, so great in its achievements of discovery, could be so low spiritually as to give up thinking."*
>
> ALBERT SCHWEITZER,
> "Life and Thought."

THE THEME throughout this book has been that evolution is constantly bringing new forms of life into existence—and that creation is a continuous process. We have attempted to show man as the product, not merely of a limited biological development, but as an inherent facet of cosmic evolution.

We have seen how the background materials of the universe organize themselves in a special way to become great whorls of gas and star-packed galaxies and how the earth, tethered to one of the myriads of stars of a single galaxy, has brought forth the phenomenon of life.

In a unique experiment carried out at the University of Chicago in 1953, Stanley Miller showed that amino acids, which are the basis of protein, can be produced quite readily by electrical energy acting on water, methane, ammonia and hydrogen—the possible constituents of the earth's primordial atmosphere. On the larger scale, sunlight acting upon a "soup of organic compounds" in the earth's primitive seas is believed to have triggered the transformation of inert matter. There is the alternative theory that life had an atomic origin.

The classical theory of life's beginning in the sea may be valid or, like many other theories before it, it may have to be modified if evidence subsequently comes to light that life has evolved on planets which may never have possessed large bodies of water. At any event, there is growing evidence that life's beginning was less precarious than we had earlier supposed. And since sunlight is the common property of the universe, there is nothing to suggest that the millions of other planets which may exist having the right dimensions, chemistry and distance from the parent suns, may not be equally favoured, Creation has not ceased either on the biological or the cosmic level. In the Milky Way, and in all other galaxies too, stars are being born in their millions. New stars—and presumably planets as well—are continually forming out of the tenuous hydrogen clouds.

However, lacking direct evidence, we cannot *prove* the existence of extra-terrestial life. And yet, when we contemplate the myriads of other suns in the heavens, it is difficult to believe that out of all this great assembly man is alone. Contrary to the spokesmen of religion, who insist that "the Universe was created by God for Man," we are disposed to the view that in the gardens of creation, there are many trees and many fruits, which seed and propagate in wide profusion.

What *facts* have we obtained? Few enough, it is true, with the limited means at our disposal, yet sufficient for us to be fairly sure that, at least on Mars, a primitive form of plant life has come into existence. Nothing spectacular, perhaps—no signs of the activity of intelligent beings beloved of scientific fiction—but nevertheless indications that some kind of life may have come into being elsewhere than on our own planet.

We assume, at least as far as earth-life is concerned, that man stands at the head of evolution, yet a million years hence, the same natural processes that brought man into existence will have created new progeny whose relationship with ourselves may be as far removed as our present relationship is with the tree-dwelling primates. There is, on the other hand, the distinct possibility that, like so many other creatures before him, man will prove unequal to his environment and will become extinct. Indeed, he has already manufactured for himself an environment in which this course seems quite possible—and it is small consolation to reflect that this would be a logical and wholly just fate for so quarrelsome a creature.

Today, the hydrogen-bomb threatens the whole of civilization and man is divided against himself. Overnight, the method of settling international disputes by open conflict has become unprofitable—and yet the human species has not evolved sufficiently to be able to work out a solution that does not depend upon force. We have many slogans: "Ban the Bomb!"—"High-level Talks"—"Aerial Inspection"—but the fact remains that so long as man remains as he is, there can be no permanent solution. There may be temporary political expediencies; the widespread fear that the hydrogen-bomb could wipe out both warring groups may be a deterrent to open conflict, but a world that is divided by fear cannot expect to survive for ever. Something must supersede the present uneasy era.

Although evolution can bring about great changes on a biological level from which new species will continually develop, the process is one that can scarcely hold great promise in man's present dilemma. However, the degree of intelligence that gave man dominance over the animals—without which he would surely have perished in the primeval forest— is again the factor that may be his salvation. He has the faculty that other creatures have not possessed—the ability to reason objectively about his fate. Indeed, the stark reality of the hydrogen-bomb may become the very factor that initiates the "chain reaction" that changes man's path of evolution toward an utterly different mode of life. If it has done nothing else, it has set people throughout the world thinking about vital problems. It has lifted them above the trivialities of everyday routine. People are beginning to inquire more and more about the world in which they live, and there is everywhere a genuine desire for understanding.

To continue as we are is clearly impossible. The evidence of past failure is recorded for all to see—and just one more would be catastrophic.

For the present, the chances are that fear of retaliation will prevent the weapon from being used, but there can be no certain security and we can only rely on this as a breathing space. So, for the moment, we must expect the "cold war" to continue with East or West stopping short only at the threshold of global conflict.

How long the peoples of the world remain locked in the grip of this incredible struggle, with its growing potential of destruction, it is impossible to predict. Only the Ice Ages which once seemed destined to erase all life from the earth can parallel the situation that confronts us today. But, like the Ice Ages, the danger may recede.

As radio-active dust clouds spread high into the stratosphere over testing grounds in the Pacific Ocean and the wastelands of Siberia, the morality of war itself is being questioned. Not because the H-bomb is a greater evil than man's more primitive weapons but simply because, in the face of such immense destructive power, armed conflict on a global scale has ceased to be a practical proposition. In view of this, at least for a short period, the hydrogen-bomb may do what centuries of moral teaching have failed to do!

It is easy to find scapegoats for our plight. We blame the scientists who produced the bomb. We blame the generals for planning to use it. And we blame the politicians for sanctioning its use. The one thing we overlook is that such discoveries as resulted in the H-bomb are inevitable in the human make-up, simply because of the particular path our evolution has taken. Were it not so, we should have remained creatures of the forest.

"The fault, dear Brutus, is not in our stars, but in ourselves . . . "; in our failure, in the midst of our discoveries, to grasp the real essentials of life, and face up to our responsibilities as conscious thinking beings. How can we, who pretend to intelligence, sanction the famine that exists in a world of plenty, and the continuence of mass slaughter for political ends? That man, with his proud brain, could have progressed so far in the acquisition of knowledge, and in the conduct of his affairs have remained so close to the temperament of the savage, is the eternal paradox.

What solution is possible until people throughout the world become aware of the waste of human effort that exists in the ruthless customs and rituals which divide and regiment the human race? Just think of all the propaganda which, day after day (mostly without malice) is poured out upon the world through every medium of human communication, newspapers, radio, T.V., and film—to schoolchild as well as adult—the only result of which is to puff up national prestige, nation over nation, West over East, East over West, religion against religion, dogma against dogma. If such media could be used instead to break down these barriers and employed to unite people under a common bond of selfless understanding, there would be no question of the outcome. Instead of people's minds being filled with the particular " dogma " of their own geographical location, they would be encouraged to expand mind and personality, to embrace a world outlook. We should still have a long road to travel—for the change must come from *within* man, and no external influence is likely to suffice by itself—but at least it would eliminate the stream of negative ideas which maintain class, racial and national hatreds, and provide an opportunity for re-establishing our civilization.

At present, such ideas exist only at the pinnacle of idealism, and yet in the world today there is a growing force that must eventually find full expression. In the Soviet-dominated satellite states, ordinary men and women are demanding the right of freedom from political slavery. In the southern states of North America and in Strydom's South Africa, ordinary men and women are demanding freedom from racial oppression. The plain truth cannot be emphasized too strongly, that domination, whether of race, ideology or religion, cannot succeed.

In an age of expanding horizons, people are becoming increasingly aware that freedom and independence are fundamental, and one should not be surprised if this outlook does not have its influence in every field of human activity.

It is not entirely coincidental that science, in abandoning the dogmatic concepts of the last century, has come out in favour of an abstract reality existing behind the world of matter, which has disposed for ever of the idea that man holds the centre of the stage. Man looks out from his " speck of dust " and finds no measurable bounds to the cosmos. He peers closer and closer into the atom until nothing meets his gaze but the shadows of waves; and under his penetrating inquiry the universe itself dissolves into formless fields of interpenetrating energy. What was once solid ground beneath our feet is now revealed as of more subtle form.

The pure scientist's ever deepening humility as he delves further into the microcosm and the macrocosm surprises specialists in more mundane fields. But, in the more general sense, his example is paving the way to a broadening of understanding among people who can no longer accept rigid systems of belief and who are striking out to seek truth for themselves.

One of the great disasters of our Age is our lack of faith in the value of moral ideas.

Christendom has great international strength and one would have imagined it would be vigorous and outspoken, for example, on the question of apartheid and racial oppression. Yet when the voice of a lone Christian priest is raised in anguish at "dark-age" intolerance in South Africa, he is hastily withdrawn from his mission. A great English churchman is invited to comment on the Church's attitude to "blood sports," and can only reply that its attitude has never been defined.

Instead of moral leadership, the Christian Church lines up squarely behind the politicians. Dr. Cyril Garbett, the late Archbishop of York, supported the manufacture of the hydrogen-bomb. Many other Church-leaders followed him. It is a sad commentary on the way organized religion has distorted the example of the Founder.

In an age when people everywhere are crying out for moral leadership, one would have thought the Christian world would have been among the first to take up the challenge. But, alas, there is no moral bridge being built into the future, and the example of Jesus is lost amid the relentless ceremonies and rituals which are the Church's constant preoccupation.

One could find many Church-leaders who are convinced that anything short of supporting the manufacture of the H-bomb as a deterrent would be impractical. It should be unnecessary to remind them that, in his day, Jesus was "impractical," his teaching in great conflict with the established teaching of his time. Ideas that conform to the world around us are not what we need, but a revolution that eventually will take a hold in all human affairs.

To meet the problem, we must learn to think again from basic principles—we must recognize that unlike the natural barrier of ice that saw the end of many creatures before us, the problem of our time is non-physical and dwells within ourselves.

At present, we appear to be in the midst of what some authorities are pleased to call a "Religious Revival," which is clearly a reflection of the uncertainties and despair of the Atomic Age. Psychology has the answer: at a time when life seems insecure and apparently without purpose, religion fulfils a vital need, and the more certain a religion may be in the authority of its dogma, the greater is the sense of security it affords. The dogma may bear no relationship with contemporary knowledge, yet for millions of people, it is "good therapy."

There are, on the other hand, many people who find no satisfaction in such affiliations; they feel instinctively the pulse of life, the vitality that is nature's every moment. If nature is like that, they will say, must the evolving human mind be shaped and moulded by convention and its creativeness dulled by repetition?

What have the world's leaders to say of the atomic problem? "We will tirelessly endeavour to bring about, by way of international agreements—always in subordination to the principle of legitimate self-defence, the . . . banishment of atomic, biological and chemical warfare."[1] This statement is typical of many. In other words, despite the evidence of past history, we must continue to build upon the existing moral and political structure, with all the evidence of the failure of international agreements and the attempts of various political factions, to establish peace from the debris of recurring conflict!

On this score, there seems precious little hope for mankind, for what is overlooked is that the solution to the H-bomb demands measures as revolutionary as the weapon itself. The truth is that its development has rendered the present world system completely obsolete. It has brought the end of an era!

Yet the "solutions" we offer to meet the dark challenge of our Age are the same "solutions" we have tried before, the matching of force with force, international agreements, militant Christianity—the same weary round of ideas which have failed us time and time again.

[1] From the Pope's Easter message, 1954.

The stark reality of the situation has yet to dawn. *It is no use trying to build on the crumbling foundations!*

Again, one cannot help drawing the analogy of the dinosaurs, where a new age brought a changing environment to which they simply were not capable, physically, of adapting themselves. However, whereas the dinosaurs could only expect to evolve on a biological level, man having reached a higher rung of the evolutionary ladder is better equipped for the task.

Yet unlike the environment which eclipsed more primitive creatures, the environment which threatens to eclipse man is of his own making. If a future Ice Age were to threaten him, man might survive it by building great underground cities and heating his subterranean home with atomic power; this is the kind of challenge his temperament could meet. But the danger that threatens him today is man-made!

Man has no alternative than to re-examine the whole basis of his culture and learn to think again from the beginning. There is no easy solution and many beloved conventions must fall by the wayside as the Old World gives way to the New.

We live in a changing, exciting world, in which, paradoxically, the brightest and most hopeful prospects for mankind exist in company with the darkest hazards.

BIBLIOGRAPHY

THE following is not intended to be an exhaustive bibliography. Most of the books listed are of recent publication, but where it is impossible to obtain personal copies, they may often be borrowed from the local Public Library. The local libraries are generally most helpful in assisting technical readers, and where they do not possess a particular volume, they have the advantage of a special national scheme whereby they can draw freely upon the resources of every other library and can usually obtain any desired work within a few days.

ASTRONOMY AND ASTROPHYSICS

The Nature of the Universe, by FRED HOYLE. Basil Blackwell, Oxford, 1950.

The popular series of broadcast talks in book form, summarizing contemporary knowledge in the fields of astronomy and astrophysics.

Frontiers of Astronomy, by FRED HOYLE. William Heinemann, Ltd., London, 1955.

A more technical work than *The Nature of the Universe*, outlining the new picture which modern astronomy and atomic physics have given us. Considers an alternative theory of the earth's origin which suggests that the inner planets may first have condensed as a swarm of small rocky particles, instead of directly from incandescent gas; also, that the first step towards life may have taken place while the mass of cold particles was still distributed in space, in which condition, the planetary material would intercept a much higher proportion of the "life-building" ultra-violet light emitted by the sun.

The Changing Universe, by JOHN PFEIFFER. Random House, New York, 1956.

The story of radio-astronomy which is opening up a rich and unsuspected source of discovery.

Man and the Planets, by R. S. Richardson. Frederick Muller, Ltd., London, 1955.

A concise, up-to-date, and highly readable account of man's present knowledge of the planets by a distinguished American astronomer.

Guide to the Planets, by Patrick Moore, F.R.A.S. 1955.

Guide to the Moon, by Patrick Moore, F.R.A.S. 1953.

Guide to Mars, by Patrick Moore, F.R.A.S. Frederick Muller, Ltd., London, 1956.

Three books by a well-known British astronomer which cover every important aspect of the solar system in a straightforward and mainly non-technical way; including useful tips for the amateur astronomer.

Earth, Moon and Planets, by Fred L. Whipple. J. and A. Churchill, Ltd., London, 1946.

One of an authoritative series entitled, *The Harvard Books on Astronomy*. Other titles include, *Between the Planets* (dealing with comets and meteors), *Our Sun, Galaxies, The Milky Way*, and *The Story of the Variable Stars*.

The Atmosphere of the Earth and Planets, by G. P. Kuiper. University of Chicago Press, U.S.A., 1949.

A collection of papers giving the latest observations and theories regarding planetary atmospheres.

BIO-CHEMISTRY, BIOLOGY, AND THE NATURAL SCIENCES

The Origin of Life (contributions by J. B. S. Haldane, J. D. Bernal, N. W. Pirie and J. W. S. Pringle). New Biology 16, Penguin Books, London, 1954.

Observations on the enigma of life by four distinguished biologists (The Origins of Life), Haldane; (The Origin of Life), Bernal; (On Making and Recognizing Life), Pirie, and (The Evolution of Living Matter), Pringle.

Light, Vegetation and Chlorophyll, by J. Terrien, G. Tuffaut and J. Carles (translated by Madge Thompson). Hutchinson, Ltd., London, 1957.

Deals with the requirements and utilization of light by plants, and with the chemistry of chlorophyll and photosynthesis.

Animals Without Backbones, by RALPH BUCHSBAUM. Penguin Books, London, 1951.

The story of the amœbas, sponges, corals, jelly-fishes, star-fishes, worms of all kinds, insects and the variety of invertebrates which make up 95 per cent. of the animal kingdom—a serious scientific work which is as attractive to read as any natural history.

Life on Other Worlds, by SIR HAROLD SPENCER JONES. The English University Press, London, 1940 (revised edition 1954).

The former Astronomer-Royal's own contribution on the question of life arising elsewhere in the universe.

Life and the Universe, by THE EARL NELSON, F.R.A.S., F.R.G.S., F.R.S.A. Staples Press, Ltd., London, 1953.

A popular survey of the universe, with chapters dealing with the expanding universe, the sun and other stars, the atom, radiation, the origin of living matter, the first animals, earth-quakes and volcanoes, hurricanes, tornadoes, waterspouts and lightning.

The Green and Red Planet, by HUBERTUS STRUGHOLD. Sidgwick and Jackson, London, 1954.

Brilliant definition of the biological possibilities on Mars, with results of original research, by the Head of the Department of Space Medicine, U.S. Air Force School of Aviation Medicine.

Evolution—the Modern Synthesis, by JULIAN HUXLEY. George Allen and Unwin, London, 1942.

An anthology of evolution as expressed in animal life.

PHYSICS (AND RELATIVITY)

An Approach to Modern Physics, by PROFESSOR E. N. DA C. ANDRADE. G. Bell and Sons, Ltd., London, 1956.

An up-to-date appraisal of developments in the sphere of atomic physics, including the investigation of cosmic rays and the extraordinary particles to which they give rise; other subjects dealt with include ultra-sonics, radio-astronomy and the properties of matter in the neighbourhood of absolute zero.

Contemporary Physics, By C. V. WEIZSÄCKER and J. JUILFS (translated by A. J. Pomerans). Hutchinson, Ltd., London, 1957.

A survey of the entire field of physics, both classical and contemporary. Gives a sound conception of what physics has achieved and what it is up to, without the use of mathematics.

The Universe and Dr. Einstein, by LINCOLN BARNETT. Harper and Brothers, New York, 1948; Victor Gollancz, Ltd., London, 1950.

A popular account of the universe in the light of modern scientific and cosmological theory, with special reference to Einstein's classical theories.

PHILOSOPHY, PSYCHOLOGY, THEOLOGY AND MYSTICISM

The Mystery of Lourdes, by RUTH CRANSTON. Evans Brothers, Ltd., London, 1954.

A sensitive and quite fascinating account of the healings at the world-famous shrine, with full medical evidence.

Power of the Mind, by ROLF ALEXANDER, M.D. Werner Laurie, London, 1956.

Sets forth the basic philosophy of Creative Realism developed by the author through original research and development over a period of forty years, giving step by step exercises by which the power of consciousness may be heightened.

The Imprisoned Splendour, by RAYNOR C. JOHNSON, M.A. (Oxon.), Ph.D., D.Sc., (Lond.). Hodder and Stoughton, London, 1953.

An approach to reality, based upon the significance of data drawn from the fields of natural science, psychical research and mystical experience.

An Experiment with Time, by J. W. DUNNE. Adam and Charles Black, Ltd., London, 1927.

Describes a series of close observations of dreams suggesting that the dreamer was often aware of events which occurred in his waking life *after* he had dreamed about them. The explanation put forward by the author involved a new conception of the nature of time.

The Serial Universe, by J. W. DUNNE. Faber and Faber, London, 1934.

Mathematical sequel to *An Experiment with Time*, dealing with space-time serialism.

The Doors of Perception, by ALDOUS HUXLEY. Chatto and Windus, London, 1955.

A fascinating account of the author's experiences during a series of experiments with the drug Mescalin in which the powers of perception were heightened and changed and the sense of time transformed.

The Undiscovered Country, by H. S. MILLIGAN. Robert Hale, Ltd., London, 1952.

Reflections about the mysteries of God and the universe—man and his destiny, faith and dogma, and various aspects of human behaviour.

God is my Adventure, by ROM LANDAU. Faber and Faber, London (new edition, 1942).

A book on modern mystics, masters and teachers.

The First and Last Freedom, by J. KRISHNAMURTI. Victor Gollancz, Ltd., London, 1954.

At last—a book written for general publication in which Krishnamurti, in his unique and uncompromising way, deals with man and his problems in the search for Truth.

The Intuitive Philosophy, by ROHIT MEHTA. The Theosophical Publishing House, Adyar, Madras, India. (Obtainable from the Theosophical Society, 50 Gloucester Place, London, W.1.)

Largely based on the teachings of Krishnamurti, with interpretations on a general theosophical theme.

The Play of the Infinite, by ROHIT MEHTA. The Theosophical Publishing House, Adyar, Madras, India. (Obtainable from the Theosophical Society, 50 Gloucester Place, London, W.1.)

Application of the Intuitive Philosophy to the problems of the individual.

Comparative Religion, by A. C. BOUQUET, D.D. Penguin Books, London, 1950 (3rd and revised edition).

A survey and comparison of the great religions of the world and an examination of their contemporary significance.

The Theology of Albert Schweitzer, by E. N. MOZLEY. Adam and Charles Black, Ltd., London, 1950.

The essentials of Schweitzer's theological thought.

What is Buddhism ? The Buddhist Society, 106 Gt. Russell Street, London, W.C.1.

A reasoned exposition of the principles of Buddhism for the Western mind.

Zen Buddhism, by CHRISTMAS HUMPHREYS. William Heinemann, Ltd.

An effervescent introduction to the paradoxical world of "Zen" for the Western reader, by the distinguished barrister (President of the British Buddhist Society).

NDEX